Connie Alcala • John J. Alder • Velma "Pat" Allen • Carol M. Andrews • Bonnie Tracy Wheeler Bartels • William F. Bartels III • Robert G. Barton • Juanita P. Bedene • Robert C. Beneteau • Calvin W. Berges • Florence S. Berges • John Bergman Jr. • Pearl L. Bergman • Julia H. Boggess • J. Robert Bolton • Julia Slaughter Bolton • Henry O. Botnen • Louis Bottenberg • Jacqueline S. Brooks • Delores Carmona • Cathy Jean Carver • Theodore Cast • Gerald L. Coffey • Pamela Coffey • James S. "Sam" Cottingham • James E. Daugherty • Barbara L. Daugherty • Judith M. Davis • Richard V. DeKruyff • Christine J. DePriest Calvin Detrick Jr. • Clifton Dial • John T. "Jeff" Dixon • Lois Lorene Jenkins Duncan • Jeff Durham • Louis M. Farris • Carolyn Fiene • Delores Galvan • E.O. Gerster • John J. Glaser • Laurette Glover • Ray Glover • Richard M. Goss Jr. • Roger Grigsby • Oscar F. Grim • Helen Jean Gruening • William Gruening Jr. • Joseph Gubar • Virginia E. Hackett • Paul I. Hansen • Mary Hazelbeck • Romelia "Romey" Henson • Thomas F. Henson • Stephen Hershman • Doris M. Hill • Forest D. Hill • Richard L. Houltberg • Carl Huntsucker Jr. • Sondra Campbell Huntsucker • Eugene Jeter • Karen Jeter • Ima Jean Johnson • Robert S. Jonas • Elizabeth D. Kolega • Julia A. Lamar • Mary E. Lane • William V. Longmoor • Thomas Mahvi • Clara McClellan • Charlotte McDowell • Betty J. McLane • William L. McLane • Betty Louise Miller • David J. Miller • Vernon D. Mitchell • Susan Moberg • Sheryl Lynn Morgan • Marjorie Ann Morris • Nick Noble • Louise O'Connor • Neal O'Connor • Leona Omer • James M. Paolozzi • Jerold M. Rau • Paul H. Rinehart • John M. Rodman • Ruby Mae Scanlon • Linda L. Scurlock • Floyd Sholts • Violet Sholts • William E. Sigler • Ruth T. Sigler • Helen A. Stark • Edmund J. Stein III • Viola E. Stein • David Stover • Kathryn Anne Sullivan • Lucille M. Taylor • Anna F. Terry • Robert F. Torrey • Mary E. Torrey • John H. Tvedten Sr. • Lynn Vander Heyden • Karyn T. Walsh • Lawrence Watson • Suzanne Watson • Linda K. Wharton • Edward A. Whitney • Joyce B. Whitney • Ferna M. Wicker • Kathleen O. Wilber • James E. Williams Jr. • Paul W. Winett • Rudolph E. Zatezalo

To the victims, their families, and the many people
who helped save lives and mitigate pain during those fateful days.

THE LAST DANCE

The Skywalks Disaster and a City Changed

In Memory, 30 Years Later

•

KEVIN MURPHY
with
RICK ALM
and
CAROL POWERS

THE LAST DANCE

The Skywalks Disaster and a City Changed

By KEVIN MURPHY
with
RICK ALM
and
CAROL POWERS

Edited by
GARY MARX

Designed by
TOM DOLPHENS

Photography by

THE KANSAS CITY STAR AND TIMES (1981)

DAN WHITE

AARON LEIMKUEHLER

TODD FEEBACK

 # KANSAS CITY STAR BOOKS

Published by Kansas City Star Books
1729 Grand Boulevard
Kansas City, Missouri 64108
All rights reserved.
Copyright © 2011 by The Kansas City Star
To order copies, call StarInfo at 816-234-4636
and say "operator."
www.TheKansasCityStore.com

First edition, first printing
ISBN: 978-1-61169-012-5
Library of Congress: 2011930274
Printed in the United States.

For more about the collapse of the skywalks, see The Kansas City Star's website: skywalk.kansascity.com

TABLE OF CONTENTS

"In tribute to those who did die or were severely injured and to those who performed so remarkably well, I think there should be a memorial, one that emphasizes the positive."

— *Richard L. Berkley*

Dan White, The Star

FOREWORD

The night of the Hyatt disaster is one that will not be forgotten — nor should it be. It was a tragedy that adversely impacted the families of the 114 people killed and 200 injured.

It was also a night for Kansas Citians to be proud of because of how medical and rescue crews responded. They followed an updated plan that coordinated ambulance services and alerted hospitals to be ready for multiple emergency patients. It served victims well. In addition, the proximity of the Hyatt to several hospitals made the plan work even better.

It was not only the medical contingent but also police, fire, operating engineers and hoist operators who used their various skills to save as many lives as possible. The community as a whole also reacted extremely well by listening to pleas not to come to the area so that rescue work could proceed without interruption.

The city was stunned by the event, but we were all cognizant of the outstanding job done by all the emergency forces — both government and civilian.

On the night of the Hyatt disaster, my wife, Sandy, and I were home in anticipation of about 60 guests arriving for a charity fundraiser. It also happened to be one of the few times I did not have my police officer with me. We did have a couple of men at the house to assist people in parking their cars. We had received permission from some of our neighbors to use their driveways for parking our guests' cars. I noticed in the process that my car had been moved to one of the driveways and that there was a car parked behind it. When I saw it I asked one of the men to make sure my car was the last one in so that if any emergency came up I could leave quickly.

Ironically, about an hour later I would get such a call. Just as the first few guests arrived, I was dashing for the car and on my way to the Hyatt. Little did I realize the magnitude of what would be revealed that night and the impact it would have on our community.

Virtually the first people I saw when I arrived were Sol and Rosette Koenigsberg, who were lying on stretchers on the ground outside the hotel. Thankfully, they survived the skywalks collapse.

Upon entering the hotel I began to grasp the significance of the accident, but its magnitude and the number of casualties was unknown at that time. I could sadly see several bodies partially under the walkway. My first reaction was that there might be as many as 15 to 20 people caught in this terrible accident. I never would have guessed that the number of fatalities would rise to 114.

The police set up a command post and efficiently monitored and directed activities. I made some comments on radio and TV to encourage people to be calm and not attempt to come to the area. The fact I had been the acting mayor during the major flood in 1977 (Mayor Charles Wheeler was out of the country on city business at the time) was of great help to me.

I heard that our city attorney, Aaron Wilson, had indicated he was going to the tea dance. I tried to reach him by phone to no avail. I consequently decided to go through the makeshift morgue set up in a hotel meeting room. It was a horrific experience. We later learned that Aaron was safe.

As our dinner guests learned of the situation, they grabbed quick bites and left for home. As a result, Sandy was able to join me faster than I had expected. We remained at the hotel through the night.

We had a special city council meeting the next day — a very sad one — to ascertain what we needed to do. I determined we needed a review by an outside independent group.

The council supported a local investigation, but I felt very strongly that an outside expert was needed for a situation so tragic and significant. I did learn from Missouri Sen. Tom Eagleton, who was particularly helpful, that an organization called the National Bureau of Standards was established in Washington, D.C., to review situations such as this. I invited them to come to Kansas City.

The bureau was very professional and experienced. Investigators gathered all the information and materials from the building they could. They reviewed building codes and construction calculations. Their conclusions were very helpful in determining causes for the collapse. This led to code modification both locally and nationally.

The hospitals did a wonderful job. There were some victims who had very severe injuries — some for life. Sandy went to the hospitals numerous times, as did others. One day she picked up the phone at home and the voice on the line was that of Billy Graham, who said he would like to visit the hospitals with her. She was startled and a little uncertain but of course said that would be wonderful.

The next day the two went to hospitals. Sandy told him, when asked, that "the evening was heaven, hell and bizarre." Hell was the obvious. Heaven was the remarkable cooperation of everyone including the skills and professionalism of the police, fire, medical and engineering communities. Bizarre included balloons from the tea dance that still floated over the disaster scene that night. Graham took that description and worked it into his talk to the staff at the hospital. He also prayed with them and many of the victims. Sandy said he was one of the most inspirational, modest individuals she had ever met.

There was a sadness in the community, at the same time there was much good in the aid and assistance of so many. The cooperation of people was outstanding.

The emotions of such a terrible event are hard to describe. It left such an impact on me that it was only about two years ago — 28 years later — that I walked into the Hyatt without my eyes tearing up. In fact, they are doing that as I write this.

Aaron Leimkuehler, The Star

Mayor Richard L. Berkley

Obviously, there is a lot that we would all like to forget. However, in tribute to those who did die or were severely injured and to those who performed so remarkably well, I think there should be a memorial, one that emphasizes the positive.

Part of the memorial process is this book that explores the situation, explains the conclusions, reports on the steps for improvement and praises the brave actions, skills and support of our community. I appreciate being a part of this project.

— *Richard L. Berkley*
Mayor of Kansas City, 1979-1991

Dan White

The Skywalk Memorial Foundation board and volunteers are raising money to build a memorial to those who died, those who were injured and those who helped in the rescue effort. A website — www.skywalkmemorial.org — has been established to promote the cause and accept donations. For more on the project, please see Page 144.

INTRODUCTION

That Friday evening was typical of Kansas City in mid-summer. The city was winding down after the work-week. The weather was hot and humid. Some people had retreated to favorite restaurants or happy hour spots, others relaxed at home. Downtown was falling quiet.

Then, suddenly, sirens pierced the thick summer air. First one, then another and another, then many at the same time. Ambulances, police cars and fire trucks were rushing to the Crown Center area south of downtown.

People started to wonder and to worry.

"What are all those sirens?" Anita Gorman asked herself as she gathered with friends for a Theater Under the Stars event in nearby Penn Valley Park. "I couldn't imagine."

No one could imagine what happened that night, July 17, 1981.

Those sirens, it turned out, foretold disaster.

Two skywalks had collapsed in the lobby of the Hyatt Regency hotel, crushing scores of people gathered for the popular Friday evening tea dance. In all, 114 would die and about 200 would be injured.

The tragedy catapulted Kansas City into the national spotlight and marked the worst loss of life from a structural failure in U.S. history. It became a local version of one of those rare events — such as the JFK assassination or the 9/11 terrorist attacks — where almost everyone can remember what they were doing when they heard the news.

The tragedy shocked the senses.

"It was truly an overwhelming event," said Joe Waeckerle, an emergency physician who took charge of medical care at the Hyatt that night. "A Friday night tea dance in a brand new Midwest hotel. I don't think anyone in their wildest dreams would expect that to happen."

Almost anyone who lived in Kansas City at that time was touched by the disaster. They either knew someone who was hurt or killed or had a connection to someone through friends or family.

"It affected everyone in Kansas City in some way," said Ed Bailey, who survived the skywalks collapse.

Though it happened 30 years ago, the collapse of the skywalks is still a teachable — if tragic — moment.

Engineering students to this day are learning about design flaws that caused the skywalks to fall. Emergency service professionals use the disaster as the basis for seminars on responding to catastrophic events with high casualties.

The event even holds the attention of those born long after.

Chris Surridge, 12, spent months researching the skywalks collapse in preparation for a December 2010 educational fair at Highlands Elementary School in Mission. Chris prepared a PowerPoint called "Dancing With Disaster" that explained in detail how the skywalks fell. Most kids hadn't heard about the Hyatt catastrophe, he said.

"To know that such a big thing happened in this town is really interesting," Chris said.

The Hyatt disaster is a major part of Kansas City's history, and it is with us still.

Yet, for all the attention the event has received in classrooms, in publications, online and in network television productions, it has never been chronicled in a book that encompasses the full story. To that end, this book is being published.

"The Last Dance" is being released on the 30th anniversary of the tragedy and at a time when momentum is growing to create a memorial honoring those who died and suffered and those who aided in the rescue. A portion of the proceeds from this book will be donated to the memorial fund.

The book is dedicated to those who were injured, those who died and those who tried to save them.

— *Kevin Murphy*
July 2011

Crown Center emerged at the site of Signboard Hill, shown here in the foreground of this 1972 photograph, looking northeast. The Westin Hotel is under construction at the base of the hill, at left. Hallmark headquarters is at right. Before the decade was out, the Hyatt Regency would rise just north of the rectangular office buildings in the center.

CHAPTER 1

PRELUDE TO DISASTER

Aaron Leimkuehler, The Star; facing page Kansas City Star/Times

The Hyatt Regency hotel today is connected to the rest of Crown Center by the Link, a series of glass walkways that reach all the way to Union Station.

The Hyatt was another jewel of Crown Center, but its luster would fade barely a year later.

By Kevin Murphy

In the summer of 1981, America was losing its financial bearing. Inflation was nearly 11 percent, unemployment more than 7 percent and the country was headed into a deep recession.

Kansas City was feeling the same financial pressures. A study reported on the front page of The Kansas City Star in mid-July predicted a decade of stagnant development and little jobs growth in Missouri.

City government was struggling to keep its infrastructure from crumbling. An election was set for early August asking voters to approve a sales tax to pay for capital improvements, including new buildings for public safety and public health care.

The downtown business district was also suffering. An editorial in The Star on July 11 called downtown "often dingy, sometimes ugly" and in need of a central showcase. To address the problem, 27 major financial, commercial and corporate interests formed the Downtown Council to find solutions. They would pool ideas and resources in a drive to revive downtown.

The Downtown Council had to look no further than Crown Center a mile to the south to see revival at work. Crown Center was a booming array of shopping, lodging and entertainment offerings adjacent to the world headquarters of Hallmark Cards.

Crown Center was everything "dingy" downtown was not, but it had been in worse straits than downtown 15 years earlier.

In the early 1960s, the area was a hodgepodge of abandoned buildings, seedy businesses, rutted parking lots and billboards — lots of billboards. In fact, the area was known as Signboard Hill.

At this time, Hallmark founder Joyce C. Hall and Hallmark President Donald J. Hall, his son, decided that rather than pull up stakes and move to the suburbs they would pursue an ambitious urban renewal plan. Though privately financed through the newly formed Crown Center Redevelopment Corporation, the project would make use of tax benefits under Missouri's Chapter 353 redevelopment law, which was intended to infuse life into blighted areas.

The corporation broke ground in September 1968 on a five-building office complex, parking garage and central square. Crown Center Shops would follow in 1973, anchored by the high-end Halls department store. The 724-room Westin Crown Center Hotel opened that same year.

"Crown Center development was a real turning point for Kansas City," said Richard L. Berkley, mayor from 1979 to 1991. "It took an area that was not in great shape and turned it around. It became a little city inside a city."

Jerry Darter, city director of parks for most of the 1980s, agreed. "It became a destination," he said.

Advocates for downtown renewal, meanwhile, were not standing still, and in the fall of 1973, developers unveiled plans for a new Hyatt Regency hotel in an area bounded by Wyandotte, Central, 11th Street and 12th Street. It was to be a 1,000-room convention hotel, with a sprawling ground-level floor shaped like a pyramid and surrounded by the hotel towers.

Hopes were high for the new hotel, proposed by a local investor group called Central Redevelopment Corporation, and a grand opening was timed for the nation's 1976 bicentennial. But the downtown development group struggled to assemble financing, and the Hyatt corporation turned its attention elsewhere, to the Hall family's interest in putting another hotel at Crown Center.

A Hyatt Hotel project was first proposed for downtown, and detailed plans were unveiled in 1973 for a 1,000-room structure on 12th Street. The hotel's lobby was to be inside a soaring pyramidal atrium with towers of hotel rooms rising

from it in spiral fashion. But financing for the project faltered, and the Hyatt turned its attention to another site: Crown Center and Hallmark. In 1978, ground was broken for the $50 million, 40-story hotel at 2345 McGee St.

Downtown would have to wait for its central showcase and revival.

Discussion of the Crown Center location for a Hyatt project was made public in early 1976, and on Oct. 2, 1977, Hallmark formally unveiled plans for a 750-room Hyatt Regency hotel.

The $50 million, 40-story hotel at 2345 McGee St. would be around the corner from the Westin, giving the city a much-needed boost in drawing conventions and tourism while further elevating Crown Center's stature.

In announcing the proposed hotel, Donald Hall said the project spoke to the "economic vitality and attractiveness" of the area. It would be the only building in the Crown Center complex to rely completely on Kansas City architects and contractors. Three firms formed a consortium called PBNDML Architects Planners. Principals overseeing the project were Robert J. Berkebile, Herbert E. Duncan Jr., and Gene E. Lefebvre.

A PEOPLE MAGNET

According to The Kansas City Star, the new hotel would have 760 television sets, 457 sofas, 2,700 convention chairs and 15,120 spoons. It would employ 900 people, have two bars, one specialty restaurant — the Peppercorn Duck Club — and a full-service restaurant called the Terrace.

Dramatic architectural flourishes had become a hallmark of the upscale Hyatt chain, and chief among the desires of the developers was to build a structure that was visually arresting.

The Hyatt's owners and structural designers routinely referred to something called the "J.C. Meter" when discussing the visual impact of their hotels. They wanted designs so stunning that anyone seeing the space for the first time would exclaim, "Jesus Christ!" The more stunning, the higher the rating on the "J.C. Meter."

"There has been some joking about that," Hyatt Corp. board chairman Jay A. Pritzker would say later. "But that has never been our criteria for designing hotels."

The concept might not have been an official criterion for Hyatt and its designers, but the desire for high impact was very real.

JULY 1981

The Hyatt Regency was a source of pride for the city at a time when the economy was struggling and the daily news was full of gloom. Even our national pastime took part of the summer off. But there were diversions — a royal wedding, music and blockbuster movies — to keep us entertained.

Prince Charles and **Lady Diana Spencer** were preparing for their wedding on July 29.

Pope John Paul II was recovering from a May assassination attempt in Rome.

Singer-songwriter **Harry Chapin** died in a traffic accident in New York on July 16.

Singer **Roberta Flack** was in concert with the Kansas City Philharmonic at Starlight Theatre in Kansas City July 17.

President Ronald Reagan, who survived an attempt on his life on March 30, nominated **Sandra Day O'Connor** to be the first woman to serve on the U.S. Supreme Court.

The **Solidarity labor movement** was holding massive anti-government demonstrations in Communist-ruled Poland.

Major League Baseball was in the midst of a players strike, which revolved around a demand by teams to be fairly compensated if they lost players to free agency. The Royals, who would eventually make the playoffs, were sitting 12 games out of first place at this point.

IBM was preparing to introduce in August the **IBM Personal Computer**, the first PC, to the market.

Fifteen states, including Missouri, were holdouts in ratification of a constitutional **Equal Rights Amendment**. Lobbying was heavy as three more states were needed to reach the 35 states necessary to make the ERA the law before a June 1982 deadline.

Playing in movie theaters on July 17: **"Raiders of the Lost Ark**," "Tarzan the Ape Man," "Arthur," "Zorro the Gay Blade" and "Superman II."

Israel bombed Palestinian strongholds in Beirut and southern Lebanon, killing 300 civilians, triggering a worldwide backlash and leading to a U.S. embargo of aircraft exports to Israel.

The Crown Center project turned a blighted area just north of Hallmark Cards into a glistening office space and shopping area. The new Hyatt Regency hotel would be a late addition, eventually occupying a spot shown in the upper left-hand corner of this 1968 photo.

One of the architectural flourishes intended to achieve that impact in the new Hyatt Regency hotel would be a series of suspended walkways, aesthetically "thin and invisible," spanning the lobby atrium. The walkways, soon to be known as "skywalks," were to link the guest room tower on the north side with the meeting rooms, restaurants and other hotel amenities on the south side, 120 feet away. They would be suspended from the ceiling of the four-story hotel lobby atrium.

The skywalks — one each on the second, third and fourth floors — would be offset so that the fourth-floor skywalk would be directly above the second-floor skywalk, with the third-floor skywalk off to the side. All of them would run parallel to the entrance side of the hotel lobby on McGee Street.

On March 16, 1978, dignitaries broke ground on the new hotel with much fanfare. Dynamite used for blasting gave off green smoke, a tip of the hat to the upcoming St. Patrick's Day. Two years

When the Hyatt Regency was built, it was the tallest structure in the city, offering a commanding 360-degree view from its rooftop restaurant.

"The court has movement and color, dramatic passages and flying bridges, places to sit or stand, eat or drink and, most of all, to watch people."

Donald Hoffmann, architecture critic
for The Kansas City Star,
in a review Aug. 17, 1980

Kansas City Star/Times

later, on July 1, 1980, the mostly completed Hyatt Regency hotel held its grand opening.

On that day, Hyatt corporate executives A.N. Pritzker and Patrick Foley stood on the skywalk above the lobby, and with a twist on the traditional ribbon-cutting ceremony, Pritzker, Hall and Mayor Berkley untied three red, white and blue ribbons that had been draped from the staircase to the third-level skywalk.

The grand hotel had finally opened and in a time of economic distress in Kansas City, here was something to feel good about.

The hotel quickly became popular for its dining and entertainment offerings, including a restaurant called Skies that sat perched like a giant disc atop the hotel.

Skies slowly rotated, making a complete circle in about one hour. Windows surrounded the restaurant, offering a moving panoramic view. Skies became a novel place to take out-of-town visitors and a romantic setting for couples.

Just as much a marvel was the Hyatt's stylish and airy lobby, surrounded by a five-story atrium. The lobby was adorned with plush furnishings and carpet, flooded with light from towering windows and skylights 60 feet overhead. Fresh plants, flowers and trees gave life to the setting.

The Hyatt lobby and its surrounding conference areas and ballroom were often abuzz with meetings, parties and celebrations. It had glitz and energy.

"It was a beautiful lobby and beautiful hotel, everyone was excited about it," recalled Frank Freeman, a Kansas City businessman.

The skywalks turned out to be magnets for people to linger, socialize and watch the people and events in the lobby below.

But even then — in the midst of the gaiety and splendor of the lobby — there was an ominous note in the air. Some who were there had cast a wary eye on the skywalks.

At a party one evening, the 23rd Street Marching Cobras were playing in the lobby. One of the guests at the party was retail businessman Bob Lewellen, who later served on the city council for eight years. As the Cobras marched and drummed, Lewellen looked up to the highest skywalk.

"I remember standing there seeing that bridge jumping up and down, and I thought, 'My God, it's going to fall,' " Lewellen said.

Berkley said he, too, had wondered that first year about the stability of the Hyatt skywalks and about fashionable architecture in other hotel lobbies and public spaces of that period.

"It was an era when structures were built with creative designs," Berkley said. "We thought the engineers knew what they were doing."

"TEA DANCING TONIGHT"

In May of 1981, the Hyatt decided to draw on the popularity of the hotel's lobby by hosting Friday night tea dances, a throwback to another generation, which had proven successful at its hotels in other cities. Steve Miller and the Hyatt Regency Orchestra started playing at 5 p.m. and dance contests would begin at 7.

Songs were from the big band era of the 1930s, '40s and '50s, featuring the tunes of Benny Goodman, Count Basie, Duke Ellington, Clark Terry and others.

A story in The Star on May 28 called the free entertainment "relaxed new-fashioned fun." The writer suggested that people who didn't dance might still like to watch from the sunken lounge in the lobby or from the balconies and upper walkways.

The weekly tea dances in the new hotel's lobby featured music from the big band era and quickly became a popular draw.

Kansas City Star/Times

The eighth tea dance of the year was on July 17, on the evening of a hot summer day. Attracted by a cool space and swinging music, about 1,500 people showed up.

The dances drew a lot of people old enough to remember the big band era, but younger couples and singles also showed up. Beer and soft drinks were $1, wine and liquor $2. The Hyatt was the place to be on a Friday night.

"Everybody was talking about it," Freeman said. "A couple of folks from work said, 'You really ought to go, it's a great place for networking, lots of people, great fun.' "

The dances had not only become popular with older couples who remembered big band music but drew singles and the after-work crowd, said Rich Coble, who played the trombone in the Steve Miller band on Friday nights.

"It was a party," Coble recalled. "It was laid-back, the work week's over, the ties are loose, you don't have to deal with rush-hour traffic."

An estimated 1,500 people would usually show up for the tea dance. "It turned out to be even more than the Hyatt anticipated," Coble said.

The eighth tea dance of the year was held on Friday, July 17. People started arriving at 3 p.m., saving the best seats as they mingled and socialized — a nice respite from the 90-degree heat outdoors.

By 4:30 p.m., downstairs seats were full and new arrivals went

The second-floor skywalk was a prime space to watch the dancers and the band below. The photos on these and the following pages were taken during a tea dance in May 1981.

upstairs to tables overlooking the lobby. Some people started gathering on the skywalks.

That same early evening, Mayor Berkley and his wife, Sandy, were greeting guests at a fundraising party at their home near Ward Parkway. Berkley looked out and saw someone had parked behind his car. He was concerned about being blocked in so he asked the police officer who served as his driver to have the other car moved.

"I told him, 'You never know when I might have to leave in a hurry,' " Berkley said.

About 6:30 p.m., back at the Hyatt, Freeman arrived with his partner, Roger Grigsby, and after a while they went up to take in the view from the skywalks. There were only a few people up there then, Freeman said.

John and Fran Calovich of Kansas City mingled with others on the fourth-floor skywalk. They were at the Hyatt for John's high school reunion. The couple wasn't comfortable on the skywalk because it swayed, John said.

"I wanted to get off of there, it didn't feel right to me," he said. The Caloviches returned to the lobby on the ground floor.

Meanwhile, John and Marie Driscoll of Lee's Summit were chatting in the lobby with three other couples they had come with to the dance. They were among scores of people directly below the second-level skywalk, watching the dancers. A drink line also formed under the skywalk.

"It was real crowded," John Driscoll recalled. "My wife didn't want to dance and one of the other couples said, 'Why don't we go up on the mezzanine and get something to eat?' " They took the escalator to the next level and got in line to be seated.

At that same time, Freeman and Grigsby had returned to the lobby under the skywalks, in effect switching positions with the Driscolls.

As they waited, Driscoll noticed KMBC-TV newsman Micheal Mahoney and his cameraman, Dave Forstate. The Driscolls were standing only a few feet from Mahoney and Forstate, who had been filming the dance for a feature story and were changing the tape and battery for the camera.

Below, Grigsby went to the south lobby bar and returned with vodka tonics. The dancers wore numbers on their backs as the dance contest was just getting started to the sound of Duke Ellington's "Satin Doll."

Freeman spotted an interesting older couple on the dance floor. He pointed them out to a woman standing near him, and said, "Look ..."

The time was 7:05 p.m.

10

CHAPTER 2

THEN THE MUSIC STOPPED

With a sudden snap and a deafening crash, a dreamy evening turned into a horrific nightmare.

By Kevin Murphy

Barbara Nesser was standing at the railing of the second-floor mezzanine when she casually glanced up at the fourth-floor skywalk. Several people were up there, looking down at the dancers and spectators on the lobby floor.

Then, in horrifying disbelief, Nesser saw it happen.

Snap! Snap!

Long steel vertical rods that had suspended the fourth-level skywalk from the ceiling suddenly let go, first one, then another, and another. The skywalk, 120 feet long and weighing more than 30 tons, buckled and fell with devastating force.

"It broke in the center and went down, down, down," Nesser said. "It was so instant."

The second-floor skywalk, 30 feet directly below, fell too, and both structures crashed to the lobby floor, and pancaked with a deafening roar and a thick white plume of concrete dust.

Kathy Morton was in the lobby and just missed being buried in the wreckage.

"It was the loudest sound I had ever heard," Morton said. "It was like a big bang."

John and Marie Driscoll, standing on the mezzanine, also heard

Kansas City Star/Times; photo opposite: Greg B. Smith, The Times

The collapse severed an overhead pipe that sent water streaming onto the chaotic scene for almost 40 minutes while rescue workers struggled to free the injured and the dead.

15

Gary Jenkins

The first fire trucks were arriving, and it was chaos. I remember standing next to a TV camera crew looking inside and seeing the destruction of the skywalks collapsed. There was moaning and crying and arms and legs protruding, and we just stared helpless. The camera guy did not even shoot the video.

the skywalks break loose and slam to the floor.

"To me, it sounded like two rail cars backing into each other," John Driscoll said. "I looked to where the noise came from, and I saw this huge piece of stuff go down. Everything to me was like in slow motion. My brain couldn't believe what my eyes were showing me."

The impact shattered the tempered glass side rails on the skywalks, spraying massive amounts of broken glass that flickered in the sunlight that streamed through the lobby windows, Driscoll recalled.

Then, there was silence.

"There was no noise, nobody crying, nobody shouting, it was stillness," said Dorothy Dixon, who was on the second-level skywalk with her husband as it fell. "I think everyone was in a state of shock."

But in seconds, silence gave way to chaos.

People screamed. They called out and groped in the dust and in the darkness for people who had been with them. Survivors crawled frantically over rubble. And mangled bodies.

A woman raced to a telephone and reached a fire department dispatcher at the alarm office a block away.

"Come to the Hyatt Regency immediately!" she pleaded. "Three skybridges fell in ... bridges holding people ... fell and crushed."

At 7:08 p.m., three minutes after the collapse, fire crews were dispatched to the scene.

Calls came in rapid succession to the fire alarm office.

Dispatcher Phil Wall ordered an ambulance to the Hyatt as chief dispatcher Dean Gurney sounded an alarm that sent three pumpers, a ladder truck and a battalion chief to the scene.

"Some sort of structural collapse at the Hyatt Regency hotel, 2345 McGee," Gurney said. Wall alerted the life flight helicopter at St. Joseph Hospital to stand by.

Seconds later, a Kansas City police dispatcher at headquarters downtown received her first call from the Hyatt. It was from an off-duty police officer inside the hotel.

"Dispatcher? Jesus, yeah," he said. "We need help at the Hyatt. We need something that can lift several tons. We need the fire department. People are trapped underneath the balcony."

Fire dispatcher Larry Gonnello summoned a fire truck with hydraulic tools.

Police officer Vince Ortega responded to the front of the Hyatt minutes after the collapse.

"People were coming out screaming, full of blood and trying to drag me to the scene inside," Ortega recalled. "I was being pulled from all different directions."

Ortega said that when he walked into the lobby, he smelled a mixture of blood, alcohol and water. Bodies were pinned down by the rubble. Other injured people, knocked down by the skywalk or falling debris, lay motionless on the floor.

"I just felt helpless," Ortega said. "There was so much chaos, so many bodies. I got on the radio and asked them to send as many ambulances as they could."

Pumper 8 was the first fire truck to arrive. It pulled into the horseshoe front drive of the Hyatt at 7:11 p.m. Battalion Chief Joe Thomas and firefighters Ray Wynn and Steve Maxwell jumped off the rig.

Hundreds of people had already fled the hotel. Some were bleeding, others in shock. What looked like gray smoke wafted from the front doors.

Thomas and Wynn entered the building and were stunned by what they found: piles of twisted metal and glass, dust and water. And bodies.

Through the haze of concrete dust, the firemen saw legs, arms and heads sticking out from the edges of the flattened skywalks. They saw contorted faces and blank, staring eyes. Blood streamed from under and around the debris, mixing with water that was pouring from an overhead pipe, a 3-inch line that snapped when the skywalks collapsed.

"I'm not prepared for anything remotely like this," Wynn said, recalling his first impressions 30 years later. "I thought, what is this? It just wasn't registering."

Wynn was 22 years old and a first-year firefighter in 1981.

The magnitude of the disaster overwhelmed many of the early responders, and some felt a sense of helplessness.

"You prepare and you train, but you never think you will have to deal with something like that."

While Wynn was finding his bearings, Thomas radioed Gonnello.

"We have people trapped .... we need heavy equipment to move it, and we need ambulances."

At 7:14 p.m., dispatcher Wall called the control center to activate a system that linked all hospitals by radio and put them on alert to possible mass injuries.

The dispatcher then ordered 10 ambulances, and at 7:16 p.m. sounded a second rescue alarm for three more pumpers and two ladder trucks. A minute later, the dispatcher requested all available hydraulic tools from the department.

At 7:18 p.m., Gonnello activated Operation Bulldozer, a program created after the devastating 1957 Kansas City tornado, to summon heavy construction equipment to the scene.

At 7:19 p.m., firefighters requested cutting tools, saws and jackhammers, anything to penetrate the concrete decks.

"We're gonna need all the tools we can get," one of them told the dispatcher, and in the next two minutes firefighters were asking for a forklift, hoping it could hoist pieces of the top skywalk off the bottom one.

More than 50 people were on the second-floor skywalk when it fell and about eight more were on the fourth-floor skywalk.

While dozens of people were crushed to death immediately, some had survived because the skywalks had cavities on their undersides between their cross supports. That gave some of the trapped victims precious space — and hope.

People trapped between the skywalks would have to be rescued either by opening holes in the concrete decks or by lifting the structure itself. Those under the bottom skywalk would have to wait until the upper one was moved.

Those who were caught under the skywalks had another worry besides

Right: While rescuers scrambled to reach the trapped and treat the injured, fire-fighters kept a wary eye on the shattered skywalks.

Next pages: The severed water line created a new set of problems for the victims and their rescuers. Hotel workers and dancers worked alongside professionals, holding IV bags for the injured and digging in the debris to reach those still alive.

Kansas City Star/Times photos

the crushing weight: a potentially deadly mix of water and electrical currents from outlets and wiring in the lobby. The broken pipe high above the lobby was pouring water onto the floor.

"If these people are not dead underneath the skywalks, they would soon be electrocuted," thought police Capt. Ron Palmer, commander of the Central Patrol Division. Those trapped under the bottom skywalk were also at the risk of drowning because water was damming up behind the lobby's glass walls and doors.

Work crews broke through the glass to release the water, and a Hyatt maintenance employee managed to shut off the water main about 40 minutes into the disaster. But standing water and slick floors remained a problem for rescue workers and victims sloshing around in it.

The fourth-floor skywalk had not fallen completely to the ground. Part of it got caught on the south wall and landed at an angle to the floor. Some people under that portion survived. Among them were Dorothy Dixon and her husband, John, who was in a wheelchair. They narrowly missed being killed by the falling skywalk, but part of the structure crushed John Dixon's chest and demolished his wheelchair. Dorothy Dixon survived with relatively minor injuries, but her husband would die four and a half months later.

While Dixon was able to crawl free of the debris and seek help for her husband, numerous victims from the second-level skywalk were pinned in the wedge between it and the fallen fourth-floor skywalk. Some were calling out for help. Wynn, the firefighter, heard some of their pleas. They were talking, trying to communicate. And he knew they were speaking their final words. There was nothing he could do.

"Once they put the call out, anybody who was licensed showed up. It was one big mess. We had to keep calm, and we had to keep people calm."

Vincent Diuguid, EMT

But there were some who could be freed more easily from the twisted wreckage. Still others were trapped in alcoves between the fallen skywalks and the bank of windows along the front of the hotel. They crawled over the skywalks to reach the center of the lobby, where they could then get care or leave the building.

Within about seven minutes after the arrival of the first ambulance, at 7:11 p.m., seven ambulances had arrived at the scene. More were on the way.

EMTs were immediately confronted with bloody and dazed victims outside the hotel. And there were more waiting inside.

Four hospitals were relatively close to the hotel: Truman Medical Center, Children's Mercy, Trinity Lutheran and St. Mary's, but care that night eventually would be provided by 17 hospitals or their personnel, including paramedics, doctors and nurses.

"Once they put the call out, anybody who was licensed showed up," recalled Vincent Diuguid, who walked to the hotel from his home and was one of the first EMTs at the scene.

Diuguid, 19 and just licensed, was directed to go immediately inside the hotel. The lobby was dark, dusty, wet and piled with debris.

"It was one big mess," Diuguid said. "We had to keep calm, and we had to keep people calm."

Within the next half hour, more than 100 firefighters, police officers, EMTs and other rescue workers would be inside the lobby. Eventually, more than 60 construction workers also would assist in the rescue, along with some people who were in the dance contest and still had numbers on their backs.

Triage was in full swing as doctors, nurses and EMTs treated in-

The catastrophic skywalks collapse in the upscale hotel instantly turned an innocent evening of summer entertainment into terrifying moments of confusion, despair and loss. No two witnesses or victims shared exactly the same experience. Their stories begin here.

FRANK FREEMAN

Frank Freeman and Roger Grigsby stood together watching the dancers. Freeman heard a pop and a crack from above. Something came smashing down. And Grigsby was gone.

"He disappeared," Freeman said. "I thought I saw him go under, but I wouldn't allow myself to believe it."

Falling concrete debris glanced off Freeman, fracturing his neck and back. He looked down to see that the giant walkway had narrowly missed him.

"The toes of my shoes touched the skywalk," he said.

Freeman had suffered ruptured discs in his neck and at the base of his spine. But he didn't scream and he didn't call out.

"I was in total shock," Freeman said. "I remember scanning the (wreckage) with my eyes and thinking, 'My God, how was this thing put together?'"

Someone — Freeman isn't sure who — helped him away from the scene.

"Then I got to thinking, 'Where is Roger?'" Freeman recalled. Freeman was taken to an employee lounge with other injured people. A police officer took him to the hospital and then called him every hour on the hour to update him on his search for Grigsby.

"The last call came at 10 a.m., and that time I refused to answer," Freeman said, sensing the worst. Finally, he picked up the phone and learned that Grigsby had died.

Aaron Leimkuehler, The Star

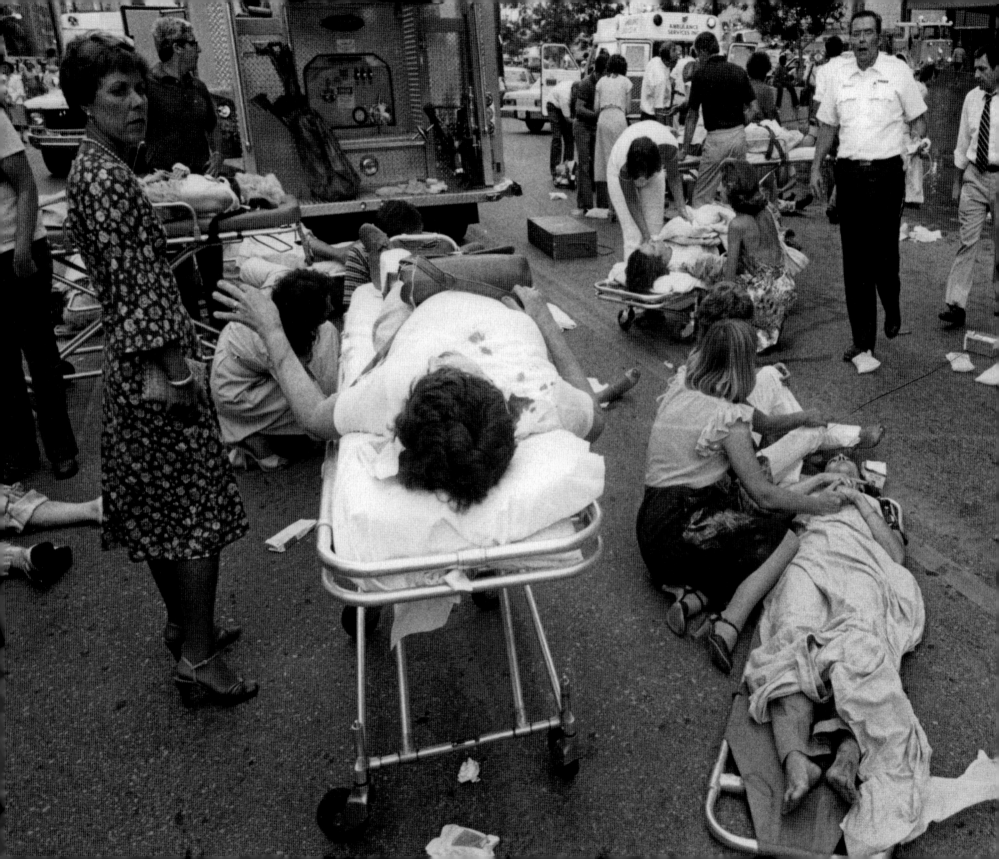

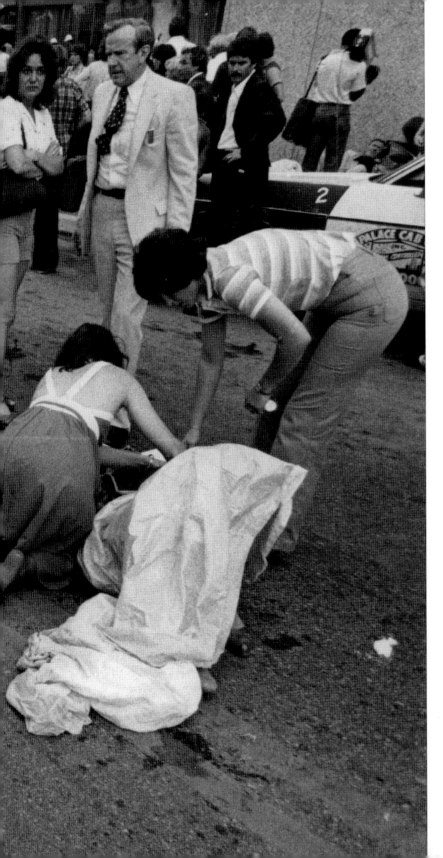

The first ambulance reached the Hyatt by 7:11 p.m. In the next seven minutes, seven ambulances would be at the scene, with more on the way.

Friends and paramedics treated and comforted the injured in the triage area outside the Hyatt.

Greg B. Smith, The Times

25

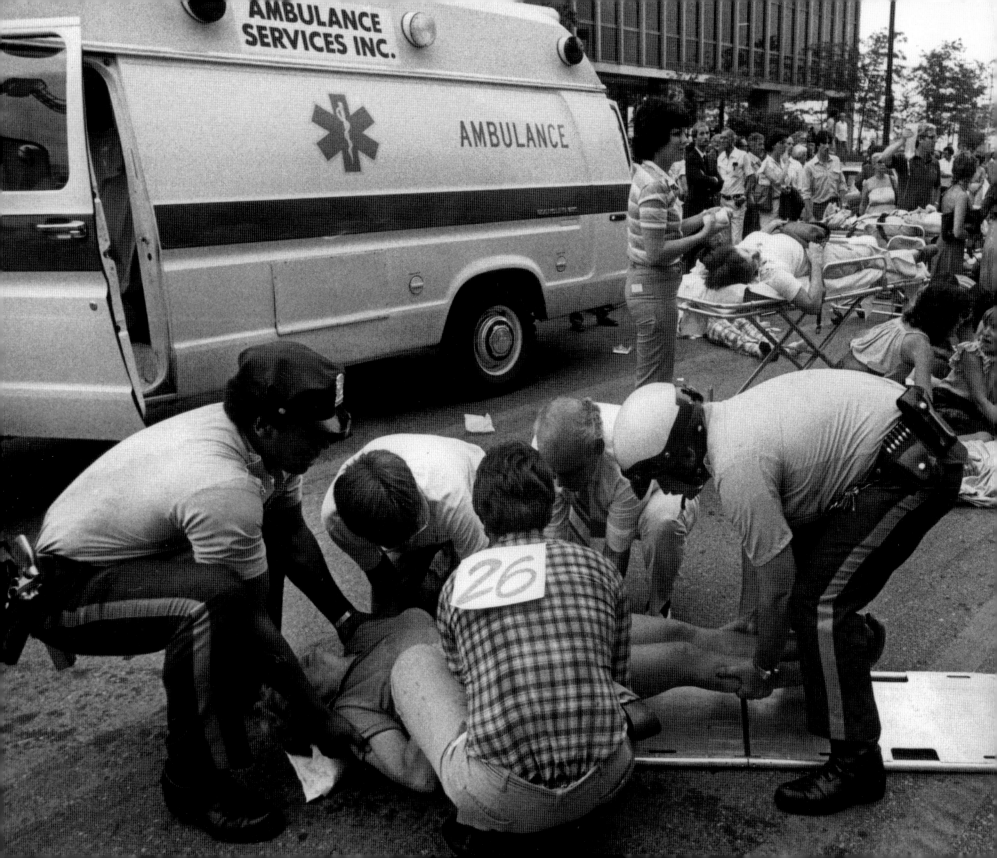

jured and trapped victims. Even bystanders helped out, holding IV vials and doing whatever they could. Relatives or friends kept vigil with some of the victims. Firemen and construction workers used jackhammers, sledgehammers, power saws and raw muscle to break through the top skywalk concrete. In some cases, they cut parts of the top skyway into pieces so they could be moved.

But single-cylinder engines needed to power the cutting tools created noise and exhaust and kicked up dust. And amid the chaos, colorful helium balloons from the dance fluttered about the dim and dusty lobby.

To clear access for forklifts, a tractor in front of the hotel tore out the revolving door, creating a fireworks of sparks and knocking out lights in the lobby.

A few minutes before 8 p.m., a forklift struggled to lift one of the skywalk segments on the south end as firemen lay on their stomachs or crouched on their knees to look between the layers.

Bigger forklifts were brought to the scene, along with a dozen Hurst tools, hydraulic lifting devices provided by fire departments in Kansas City and elsewhere.

The upper skywalk pieces were raised on one edge and then cribbed up with timbers and blocks to get access to survivors and the dead.

At about 8 p.m., rescue workers pulled a young woman from under the south end of the skywalk and then soon another woman and two

Eventually, more than 60 construction workers would assist in the rescue, along with some people who were in the dance contest and still had numbers on their backs.

27

John Spink, The Times

"Reflecting on that time makes me more aware of how precious life is and how we need to make every day count."

CHARLOTTE HOLT

Charlotte Holt was on dinner break from her job as cashier at the Terrace Restaurant and decided to watch the tea dance contest for a while from the second level.

"The sun was shining in the west, and it cast a beautiful glow throughout the atrium," Holt said. "Almost immediately my eye was caught by a lady in a red dress standing on the fourth-floor skywalk. I looked up and was amazed to see more people than I had ever seen up there before."

Suddenly, as if in slow motion, the upper skywalk broke loose.

There was great confusion in the building as people at the terrace level were unable to go out the front door, blocked by the fallen skywalks, so they fled through the kitchen, Holt said.

Holt made it outside, where people saw her Hyatt name tag and pleaded with her to go back in to look for missing friends or relatives. But that would have been fruitless.

Holt did go back in, though, and ended up helping set up a convention room for the dead and injured. It had been furnished with linen-covered tables for a floral convention that weekend.

Holt remained at the Hyatt for about three hours before leaving.

"In the weeks and months after the disaster, almost anyone you talked to either had a friend or relative die or knew someone who did," Holt said. "Lots of couples passed away that same night."

"Reflecting on that time," Holt said, "makes me more aware of how precious life is and how we need to make every day count."

Aaron Leimkuehler, The Star

"The first thing I saw were all these people coming off the elevators right at me with horrified looks on their faces."

CHERYL TAYLOR

C heryl Taylor was at the Hyatt the night of the skywalks disaster because of a floral convention her husband planned to attend. She waited for him by the front door and struck up a conversation with another woman as they watched the dancers.

"All of a sudden there was this loud noise, and I started falling down," Taylor recalled. The collapsing skywalks came close enough to knock off her purse as she fell. The woman she was talking with vanished under the fallen skywalks.

Suffering scrapes, bruises and a sprained knee, Taylor crawled out from under a pile of debris toward the lobby near the elevators. "The main thing I remember is this huge billow of dust, which I inhaled a lot of," Taylor said.

She also remembers what she saw after she crawled through the dust and rubble to the lobby.

"The first thing I saw were all these people coming off the elevators right at me with horrified looks on their faces," Taylor said. They had witnessed the collapse from the second floor and were trying to exit the building.

"I was getting trampled by people going in the opposite direction I was," Taylor said. "My husband happened to come to the front door just as the skywalks fell. He couldn't get in but found a side door. I was crawling around, he saw me and carried me out of there."

Her husband took her to nearby St. Mary's Hospital, where she was the first injured person from the Hyatt to arrive at the emergency room.

"I told them you are going to have a lot of people here, and they said, 'What are you talking about?'" Taylor said. The hospital was soon overrun with patients and Taylor was sent to another hospital and admitted.

Todd Feeback, The Star

middle-age men.

Most of the rescues would occur within the first hour. Eventually, 22 people would be found alive between the upper and lower skywalks.

Many more would not be so fortunate.

A few minutes before 8 p.m., two firemen carried a body wrapped in a blanket from a corner of the northeast lobby and placed it on a pallet near the escalator with five others. Soon, two more were added. This spot, in open view, wasn't appropriate, police determined.

Carl Glazier, a crime scene investigator in the police department, took over the job of handling the flow of bodies. Glazier found a meeting room just off the lobby where tables had been set up with flowers in vases for a floral convention that weekend.

Police officers and hotel employees cleared the tables and lined them up in what became a makeshift morgue. Victims were photographed and fingerprinted to help with the identification process. The men were easier to identify because they carried wallets while women had been separated from their purses, Glazier said.

Bodies would continue to arrive through the night. Sometimes bodies came in pieces and had to be matched up using clothing fabric, Glazier recalled. Glazier and other officers worked methodically amid circumstances they couldn't have fathomed earlier.

"It was shocking, but everybody did their job the way it was supposed to be done," he said.

There were sometimes long lulls, and Glazier would go into the lobby to watch rescue efforts.

Firefighters sometimes dug with their bare hands through pulverized concrete to reach trapped victims.

The forklifts and the Hurst tools had moved parts of the top skywalk off the bottom one, but something stronger would be needed to finish the lifting work, especially of the bottom skywalk.

11-year-old Dalton Grant and his mother, Constance Downing, were trapped under the skywalks for hours before being rescued.

Deputy Fire Chief Arnett Williams, who arrived at the scene about 10 minutes after the collapse and was acting as incident commander, recognized the need for heavy construction equipment. He had previously driven a truck and cherry picker for Belger Cartage Service, which had cranes on a project only blocks away.

The call was made and soon three heavy trucks with cranes rolled up to the front of the building. The tips of the cranes speared through the high windows above the lobby, cables were dropped to the floor, slid beneath the fallen skywalks and looped around.

The crane operators could not see what they were doing because the front of the building blocked their views, so people inside the building guided them via radio.

"Those cranes are very sensitive to the touch," fire Capt. Joe Galetti said. "The operators were real professionals at what they did. We could not have recovered those people if not for them."

The skywalks had to be lifted very gingerly so as not to further injure people trapped below, Williams said.

"If you move something on the south end, what about the north end?" Williams said. "Every action had a reaction. You had to hope and pray you were not putting anyone under there in a worse situation they had already."

Around midnight, firefighters realized there were people still alive under the bottom skywalk. One of the voices was that of 11-year-old Dalton Grant, who was trapped beside his injured mother, Constance Downing. They could barely move but could hold hands, talk and comfort each other.

Fireman Mike Trader dropped to his stomach and began talking with the boy. Trader, who had an 11-year-old son of his own, kept a conversation going with the boy while rescue workers cut holes in the top of the deck.

The boy complained about joint stiffness, from being in the same spot for so long. And for more than an hour, Trader reassured the boy

33

John Calovich

It felt as if the entire building was crashing down. The violent shaking, and deafening noise went on forever. Once the noise ceased, my wife, being an emergency room nurse, quickly made her way down to the lobby floor so she could provide medical support. I followed her to give my assistance as well. A makeshift triage area was established in the lobby where my wife was one of the first medical personnel on the scene. People who weren't trapped by the twisted metal and concrete were brought to this triage area for medical attention. To this day, I have a vivid memory of the dimly lit lobby filled with a thick concrete smoke, chaos and the cries of people seeking help.

Firefighters and rescue workers carried the injured to ambulances and loaded them into helicopters for transport to the hospitals.

Kansas City Star/Times photos

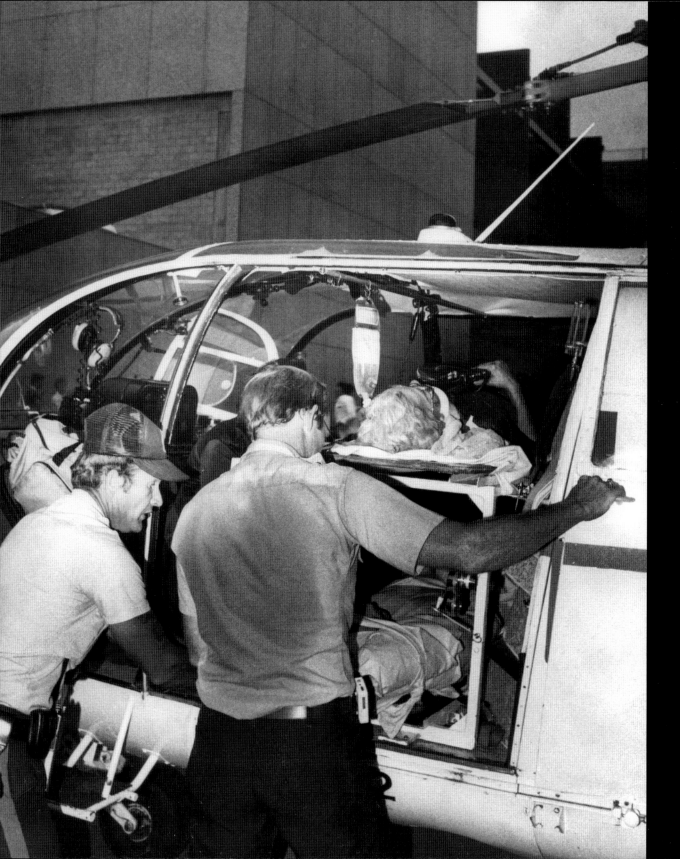

Colleen Carter

Another friend left money for us to have another drink. But after he was gone I turned to my friend and said I didn't want another drink. We got up and walked under the skywalks to the other end of the room, then up the escalator. We had a table overlooking the dance floor. I don't remember if we had ordered yet or not but as we watched the dancers down below we saw the skywalks fall. It seems like it was in slow motion.

When the boy was lifted alive from the rubble, a cheer went up among the weary rescuers. It was about 2 a.m., almost seven hours after the collapse.

that he would soon be freed.

Finally, at about 2 a.m., Dalton was pulled from a hole in the deck, to the cheers of weary firefighters and other rescue workers who had seen too many people pulled dead from the rubble.

"It was very uplifting," Deputy Fire Chief Charley Fisher recalled. "It kind of revitalized the whole scene."

Seven people were rescued from beneath the bottom skywalk, the last being Mark Williams at 4:30 a.m.

The last slab from the lower skywalk was lifted off at 7:45 a.m. Thirty-one more bodies were removed, putting the death toll at 111. In all, about 200 people were injured, many critically. Three of them would later die of their injuries.

The dead included 18 married couples.

The firefighters lost one of their own that night. Off-duty battalion chief John Tvedten, who was there for the dance, died in the collapse.

In the ensuing days, the scope of the tragedy became clear as countless people realized they knew someone who was at the Hyatt or had an acquaintance who knew someone who was there.

"You can't talk to anyone who wasn't in some way tied to that event," Fisher said.

Some 10 hours after the skywalks collapse, weary and emotionally spent firefighters, police officers, construction workers and medical professionals began going home. There was no one left to save.

It had been a long night of mostly desperation and heartbreak — one that would stick with victims, relatives, rescue workers and an entire city for years to come.

"The magnitude of it was just indescribable," Fisher said. "You never forget it."

Kansas City Star/Times

A crowd of anxious and worried people watched the rescue efforts from across the street. The emergency lasted through the night and well into the next day.

"I will say that even before I got out of the building it smelled like death."

RICH COBLE

Aaron Leimkuehler, The Star

Rich Coble had just finished playing a trombone solo in the Steve Miller band's "Satin Doll" when he detected motion above his head.

"Out of the corner of my eye, I saw kind of a movement, actually a double movement and then, 'Bang!'" Coble said.

The skywalks had crashed to the floor only a few feet from where the band was set up on risers. Band members jumped up and fled down the back of the risers toward a lobby corridor to the south, which led to an exit.

"I will say that even before I got out of the building it smelled like death," Coble said.

Outside, Coble searched for two people he knew were at the dance, but he could not find them. When he tried to go back into the building to look for them, police stopped him.

Coble suffered a gash on his leg while making his quick exit from the building. As he drove himself to an emergency room on his way home he heard a radio report that eight had died in the skywalks collapse.

"I screamed at the radio," Coble said, knowing that the death toll had to be far higher. One of the two friends Coble had been looking for earlier, Nick Noble, died, and the other was severely injured but survived.

The Steve Miller band played in a Hyatt ballroom the next year and walked through the lobby to get there.

"Everyone in the band thought that it was a little bizarre," Coble recalled. "I'm sure there were a lot of different feelings, thinking back."

Holding on

For those who labored all night, who struggled to save the lives of strangers; for those who witnessed the horror, who lost friends and loved ones; for those who waited for word … an embrace fulfilled a basic human need.

Jan Housewerth, The Star

41

12 HOURS, A CITY RESPONDS

This transcript from the Kansas City Police Department begins with the log's first entry — at 19:53 hours, or 7:53 p.m., 48 minutes after the collapse — after the KCPD command post was established. The log has been edited for brevity by dropping entire time entries, but each line listed here is verbatim.

FROM THE KCMO POLICE FILES

19:53 hours: Ordered Greater Kansas City Hospital Association.
Belger ordered; south side.
Eng. 370 shutting water off — Hotel Engineer.
20:00 hours: East side barricaded.
20:01 hours: Call in Evidence Technicians.
20:03 hours: Carl Glaiser reporting ten (10) dead bodies.
20:04 hours: Established area for temporary morgue.
20:05 hours: Major McLaury requested roster for hotel guests from manager of hotel.
20:06 hours: Fork lift being escorted by 861 from Belton, Missouri.
20:06 hours: Belger Cartage standing by at office, 19th and Forest.
20:07 hours: Radio 373 is with Building Maintenance shutting off water.
20:10 hours: Temporary morgue located south of lobby in exhibition area.
20:11 hours: Det. Sgt. Gary Adams reports a number of people wandering in and out of morgue area in hotel.
20:14 hours: Mayor Berkley arrived at Command Post.
20:17 hours: Fire Department reports two cranes is all that can be worked at one time.
20:21 hours: Cars 311, 313, 315, 331, 335, 212, 213, 221, 225, 229 in area of hotel.
20:22 hours: Tri-City en route with crane from Plaza.
20:26 hours: Major McLaury requested source to set up flood lights, electrical power, etc. (National Guard).
20:29 hours: Captain Bartlett requests crane, needs to reach 40 feet and ability to handle 50 ton.
20:31 hours: Belger sending requested crane, en route.
20:42 hours: Major McLaury requesting count from area hospitals on all casualties.
20:47 hours: Captain Kline reports 31 D.O.A.s.
20:48 hours: Third crane ordered from Belger by Major McLaury.
20:52 hours: Major Ponessa reports 36 D.O.A.s.
20:53 hours: Major McLaury informed sales manager that building should be evacuated on advice of Build-

ing Architect, in case of possible further collapse.

21:01 hours: All heavy equipment moving into area should report to 22nd and Grand.

21:02 hours: Block off second floor balcony. Generator arrived for lobby and helicopter pad, north end.

21:14 hours: Captain McKinney reports ambulance coordinator has communication with Baptist Hospital, which has complete communication with all area hospitals. This party is set up outside lobby door.

21:18 hours: Army helicopter landed at hotel.

21:28 hours: Major McLaury started hotel evacuation; all occupants to east side of hotel. There is to be NO MEDIA CONTACT.

21:29 hours: Radio 360 reports all injured have been removed.

21:33 hours: Lobby area has been evacuated.

21:43 hours: Major McLaury requests Salvation Army contact chaplains.

21:55 hours: Captain Livingston reports 40 D.O.A. First 25 D.O.A. going to TMC.

22:10 hours: All blood donors referred to Community Blood Bank. Possible need of O-Positive.

22:21 hours: 43 D.O.A.s reported.

22:23 hours: Estimate of 50 D.O.A.s from Captain Bartlett.

22:24 hours: 101 victims reported admitted to area hospitals.

22:41 hours: Captain Fred Smith reports that 25 of the 40 bodies have been identified.

23:17 hours: Captain Bartlett stated crane coming in front of building.

23:18 hours: Captain Bartlett states all okay; made safe entry.

00:00 hours: Eleven (11) relatives of deceased have been notified.

00:40 hours: Major McLaury directing all personnel with no assignment report to Command Post.

01:05 hours: Captain Mulac reports open line set up between American Red Cross at 3521 Broadway and the 28th Street Station to facilitate inquiries and notifications of next of kin, relatives of victims. American Red Cross receiving inquiries from across country.

01:35 hours: Reserve crews relieved of duty.

02:00 hours: Total of 16 police officers under Captain Palmer for ground control. One sergeant and two police officers for Command Post working injury list.

02:00 hours: One person freed; subject a live male.

02:03 hours: Two more persons freed, one female, one male.

02:33 hours: Report one female freed alive.

03:08 hours: Eight (8) bodies located under the north part of the slab. Total count now fifty-eight (58).

03:24 hours: Rain reported due at 0600 hours on 7-18-81; ½ inch or more from west; no report of any strong winds from dispatcher.

04:30 hours: Captain Livingston stated the count is now 60 D.O.A.

05:05 hours: Sergeant Connor stated moving bodies under last slab — south part of lobby.

05:07 hours: Major Moulder reported count up to 65 D.O.A.

05:23 hours: Major Moulder reported count up to 66 D.O.A.

06:54 hours: Major McLaury stated 31 bodies have been identified in person by a family member. Further, 54 bodies have been identified by some form or another.

07:20 hours: Dispatcher reported large group of people at the Community Blood Bank, 4040 Main. Metro car was dispatched.

07:30 hours: Metro car reported back that there was no immediate problem at 4040 Main, but are expecting 700 to 750 people throughout the day. Need O-Positive blood. Will call police department if problems develop.

07:35 hours: Det. Luther at TMC reports 93 bodies; 65 have been identified, 28 unidentified.

07:38 hours: Report from 304 — last portion of walkway has been raised. Last of bodies/casualties should be out within 10 minutes.

07:52 hours: Radio 304, Captain Bartlett, reports the last of the bodies have been removed and Fire Chief John Hamilton reports the emergency has ceased.

07:55 hours: Major Ponessa reports the total body count taken is one hundred and eight (108). These are the DOAs through our morgue only.

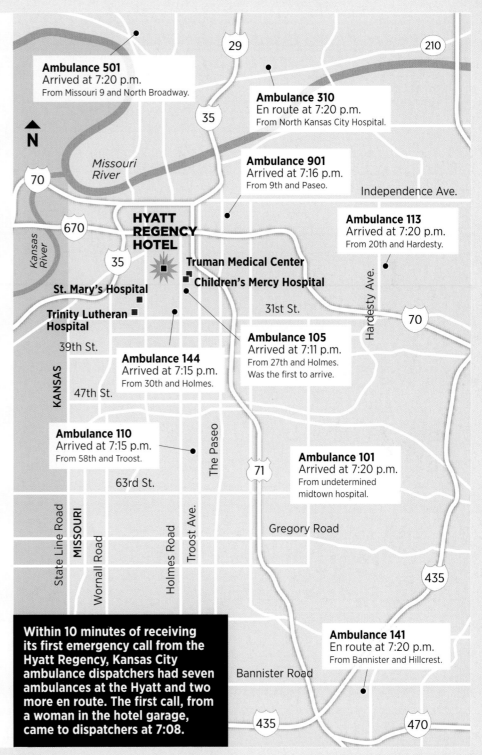

Ambulance 501
Arrived at 7:20 p.m.
From Missouri 9 and North Broadway.

Ambulance 310
En route at 7:20 p.m.
From North Kansas City Hospital.

Ambulance 901
Arrived at 7:16 p.m.
From 9th and Paseo.

Independence Ave.

Ambulance 113
Arrived at 7:20 p.m.
From 20th and Hardesty.

Missouri River

HYATT REGENCY HOTEL

Kansas River

Truman Medical Center
Children's Mercy Hospital

St. Mary's Hospital

31st St.

Trinity Lutheran Hospital

Ambulance 105
Arrived at 7:11 p.m.
From 27th and Holmes.
Was the first to arrive.

39th St.

Ambulance 144
Arrived at 7:15 p.m.
From 30th and Holmes.

47th St.

KANSAS

Ambulance 110
Arrived at 7:15 p.m.
From 58th and Troost.

The Paseo

Ambulance 101
Arrived at 7:20 p.m.
From undetermined midtown hospital.

63rd St.

Gregory Road

State Line Road
MISSOURI
Wornall Road
Holmes Road
Troost Ave.

Within 10 minutes of receiving its first emergency call from the Hyatt Regency, Kansas City ambulance dispatchers had seven ambulances at the Hyatt and two more en route. The first call, from a woman in the hotel garage, came to dispatchers at 7:08.

Ambulance 141
En route at 7:20 p.m.
From Bannister and Hillcrest.

Bannister Road

Dave Eames, The Star

Heavy lifting

After forklifts and lighter gear proved ineffective, cranes from Belger Cartage Services were pressed into action to lift the skywalks so that people could be rescued, and bodies recovered, from under the debris. Other construction companies also provided equipment, and the construction crews worked all night.

"You can't talk to anyone who wasn't in some way tied to the event. The magnitude of it was just indescribable. You never forget it."

Deputy Fire Chief Charley Fisher

CHAPTER 3

WHAT WENT WRONG

How a minor change created a major flaw and resulted in a tragedy that claimed 114 lives.

By Rick Alm

Editor's Note: On the evening of July 17, 1981, Kansas City Star reporter Rick Alm was one of the first reporters to arrive on the scene of the disaster, having dashed to the hotel from a restaurant with fellow journalists Darryl Levings and David Zeeck.

Alm would stay on the story for years, working in the days immediately after the disaster alongside an engineer who helped determine the cause of the structural failure, and later participating in a team of reporters and editors that analyzed thousands of pages of documents and produced a series of special newspaper reports on the disaster.

His story here draws upon his reporting from 30 years ago and on documents in his personal files, as well as new interviews he conducted with principals involved with the Hyatt skywalks disaster.

The damage to one of the fourth-floor box beams was clearly evident after the collapse.

Kansas City Star

When news of the Hyatt skywalks' deadly collapse shattered the calm of an idyllic mid-summer evening in Kansas City, the hotel's chief architect Robert J. Berkebile abandoned his dinner party and rushed to the scene. Identifying himself to police at the barricades outside, he was quickly escorted into the bloody, wreckage-strewn lobby.

"Once on the floor and experiencing that tragedy, I was just overwhelmed," he recalls today. "My first thought was, 'Oh my God, did I kill all those people?'"

Within days The Kansas City Star published stories detailing why the skywalks had fallen: a simple but fatal design flaw in the suspended walkways' steel support system that made their collapse inevitable. Experts, with chilling unanimity, have long agreed that catastrophic structural failure was only a matter of time.

But it would take almost five years of investigation and litigation before the first and only official finding of blame was rendered. In early 1986 the state of Missouri revoked the licenses of the hotel's structural engineers and their St. Louis firm for negligence and a "conscious indifference" to their professional responsibilities. Even-

"Once on the floor and experiencing that tragedy, I was just overwhelmed. My first thought was, 'Oh my God, did I kill all those people?' "

Robert J. Berkebile,
chief architect of the hotel

tually the engineers would be stripped of their licenses in all 26 states where any of them were registered.

Public confidence in the design professions was shaken by the fall of the skywalks' 70 tons of steel and concrete. With 114 dead and more than 200 injured the skywalks disaster still stands today as the deadliest building design failure in U.S. history.

How that flawed design came about, and the failure of so many professionals to discover and correct it before, during and after construction is a tragic tale of missed opportunities.

The skywalks fell because no one accepted responsibility to check the smallest of details to ensure their steel-to-steel connections were strong enough to hold that awesome weight. With tragic hindsight, experts agree that, had it been checked, the flawed design might easily have been fixed with about $12 worth of additional materials.

During a span of roughly 29 months, from final design concept to the collapse, warning signs repeatedly flashed that something might be wrong with the architecturally dramatic walkways that spanned the 120-foot length of the elegant Hyatt Regency hotel's four-story atrium lobby. Each time, however, those red flags were missed, overlooked or ignored.

Those who have studied the collapse find no shortage of proximate causes, among them negligence, complacency, malfeasance and the relentless financial and deadline pressures of the Hyatt's cost-conscious "fast-track construction" methods that demanded engineering and other design work stay a step ahead of simultaneous construction work. There's also the "Cool Hand Luke" theory that argues the failure to discover the flawed design was a simple "failure to communicate" among key design and construction professionals. In truth the fault lies with a measure of each.

"Everybody thought they were doing their job," Hyatt chief engineer Daniel M. Duncan, a vice president of the-then St. Louis-based affiliate of the engineering firm Gillum-Colaco, said years after the collapse at the state license hearings. "But something got through that shouldn't have."

Indeed it should not have. After years of investigation and a 26-day legal proceeding in 1984 that generated a 5,200-page hearing transcript and 450 exhibits, Missouri administrative law judge James B. Deutsch ruled in November 1985 that Gillum-Colaco engineers Duncan and company president Jack D. Gillum and the firm were guilty of gross negligence and "conscious indifference" to their professional responsibilities.

Deutsch's administrative ruling still stands today as the only official declaration of blame ever handed down by any lawful authority. Hundreds of lawsuits filed by victims or their families were all settled out of court for an estimated $140 million in damages — with no admissions of guilt or fault by anyone. No criminal court ever considered the matter. A Jackson County grand jury in 1983 cited a lack of evidence in its decision to decline to issue indictments for criminal negligence in the collapse.

About a year after the collapse more than 100,000 pages of construction documents and 15,000 pages of court-ordered depositions were made public as part of the then-ongoing court proceedings. The Kansas City Star and its now-defunct sister paper The Kansas City Times assigned a team of four reporters and an editor to the task of analyzing those records, resulting in a series of special reports in 1982 titled "The Hyatt Papers" that detailed the rise and tragic fall of the Hyatt Regency Hotel skywalks. I was a member of that team, along with fellow Star colleagues Richard M. Johnson and Roger Moore, and Times journalists David Hayes and Richard A. Serrano.

"THIN AND INVISIBLE"

During the summer of 1977 the hotel's owners and architects agreed to a concept of three skywalks, aesthetically "thin and invisible," spanning the atrium and linking the guest room tower on the north side with the meeting rooms, restaurants and other hotel amenities on the south side.

Various skywalk design concepts came and went before a

Paul Iwanaga, The Times

Robert J. Berkebile

53

system of suspended 16-inch support beams was chosen. Those assemblies — complete with a layer of concrete, handrails and gypsum board — brought the weight of each walkway to more than 35 tons. Each walkway was held aloft by three welded, 8-inch deep box beams, which were attached to six inch-and-a-quarter steel rods hung from steel ceiling beams.

While those relatively wispy rods did not fail, the scheme used to connect them to each of the 8-inch support beams did — spectacularly so.

There was confusion from the outset exactly how to make those connections work.

Under the engineers' original design, the fourth-floor and second-floor skywalks were to be vertically aligned one atop the other with both levels suspended from the same six ceiling rods. A third-floor skywalk, which also spanned the hotel's atrium, was offset to the east and did not collapse. When it was removed just days after the collapse, it was found to be in the early stages of failing in the same manner as the second- and fourth-floor assembly.

Confusion arose because the Gillum firm's design drawings did not show exactly how those six rods would connect, via nuts and washers, to and through the 8-inch beams. The drawings indicated minimal threading at the ends of each three-story long rod but did not account for how nuts and washers would be placed at the necessary points in the middle of the rods, where the fourth-floor walkway would be attached.

People "scratched their heads as to how that nut would get there," Duke School of Engineering professor Henry Petroski noted in the "Accidents Waiting to Happen" chapter of his 1982 book on building failures "To Engineer Is Human."

While the details have long been disputed, sometime in early 1979 Duncan and William G. Richey, an engineer for steel fabricator and installer Havens Steel, of Kansas City, and perhaps others, engaged in a phone conference to discuss modifying the single-rod design to a more practical double-rod scheme. It was that decision that spawned

Days after the skywalks failed, the connecting rods still hung from the ceiling where they were attached to concealed steel beams.

Kansas City Times

54

While the connecting rods did not fail, the scheme used to attach them to each of the 8-inch support beams did.

A bent steel rod, an inch and a quarter thick, protruded through one of the 8-inch box beams of the second-floor skywalk. The box beams were attached to 16-inch I-beams, which together supported the concrete deck, but all of the stress was placed on the steel rods and their connections to the box beams.

Kansas City Star/Times

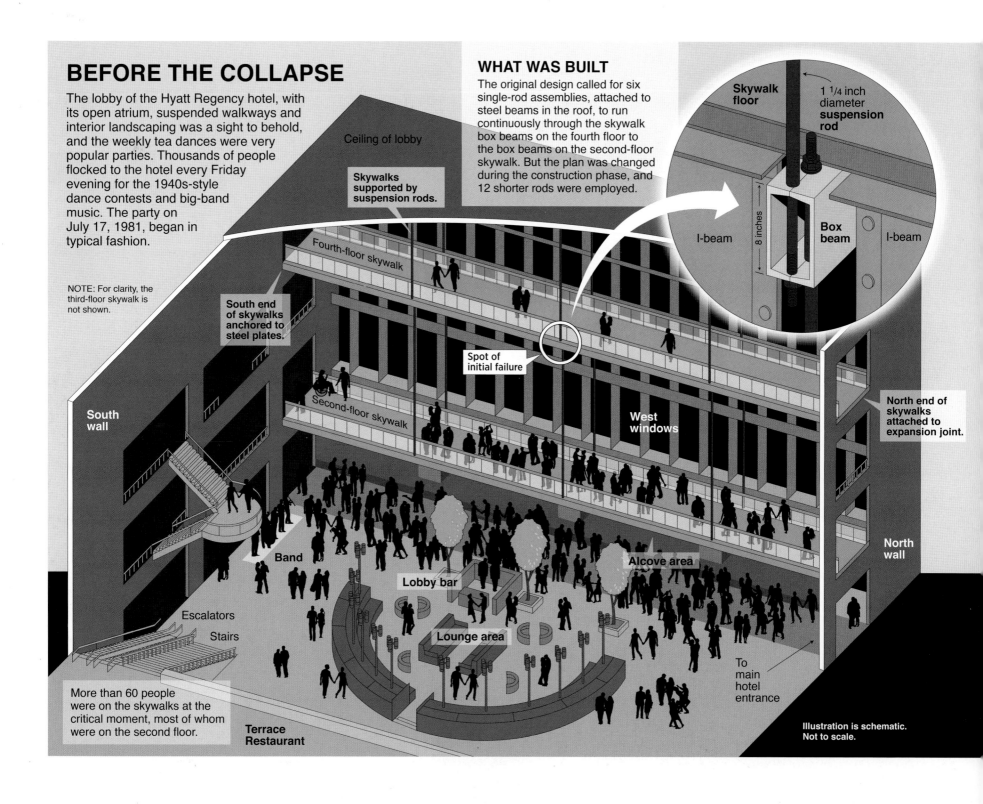

BEFORE THE COLLAPSE

The lobby of the Hyatt Regency hotel, with its open atrium, suspended walkways and interior landscaping was a sight to behold, and the weekly tea dances were very popular parties. Thousands of people flocked to the hotel every Friday evening for the 1940s-style dance contests and big-band music. The party on July 17, 1981, began in typical fashion.

NOTE: For clarity, the third-floor skywalk is not shown.

WHAT WAS BUILT

The original design called for six single-rod assemblies, attached to steel beams in the roof, to run continuously through the skywalk box beams on the fourth floor to the box beams on the second-floor skywalk. But the plan was changed during the construction phase, and 12 shorter rods were employed.

Ceiling of lobby

Skywalks supported by suspension rods.

Fourth-floor skywalk

South end of skywalks anchored to steel plates.

Second-floor skywalk

South wall

Spot of initial failure

West windows

North end of skywalks attached to expansion joint.

Band

Lobby bar

Alcove area

North wall

Lounge area

Escalators

Stairs

To main hotel entrance

More than 60 people were on the skywalks at the critical moment, most of whom were on the second floor.

Terrace Restaurant

Illustration is schematic. Not to scale.

Skywalk floor

1 1/4 inch diameter suspension rod

I-beam

8 inches

Box beam

I-beam

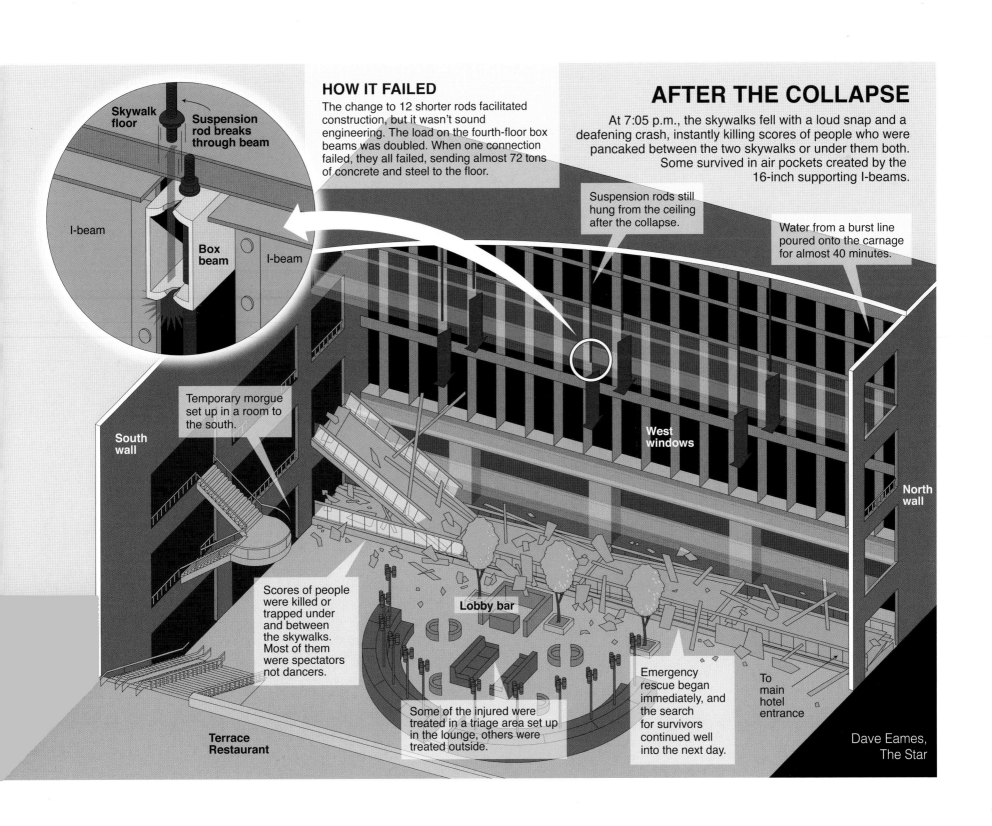

HOW IT FAILED

The change to 12 shorter rods facilitated construction, but it wasn't sound engineering. The load on the fourth-floor box beams was doubled. When one connection failed, they all failed, sending almost 72 tons of concrete and steel to the floor.

Skywalk floor

Suspension rod breaks through beam

I-beam

Box beam

I-beam

AFTER THE COLLAPSE

At 7:05 p.m., the skywalks fell with a loud snap and a deafening crash, instantly killing scores of people who were pancaked between the two skywalks or under them both. Some survived in air pockets created by the 16-inch supporting I-beams.

Suspension rods still hung from the ceiling after the collapse.

Water from a burst line poured onto the carnage for almost 40 minutes.

Temporary morgue set up in a room to the south.

South wall

West windows

North wall

Scores of people were killed or trapped under and between the skywalks. Most of them were spectators not dancers.

Lobby bar

Emergency rescue began immediately, and the search for survivors continued well into the next day.

To main hotel entrance

Some of the injured were treated in a triage area set up in the lounge, others were treated outside.

Terrace Restaurant

Dave Eames, The Star

Sometime in early 1979, Gillum-Colaco chief engineer Daniel M. Duncan and an engineer for steel fabricator and installer Havens Steel discussed plans to modify the single-rod design to a more practical double-rod scheme. It was that decision that spawned the fatal design flaw.

Daniel M. Duncan

AP

the fatal design flaw.

Later, in sworn testimony, Duncan and Richey disputed who first proposed the change and, critically, which firm was responsible for performing the necessary stress calculations. Each firm insisted those calculations were the other's responsibility.

There is no evidence that anyone ever performed those calculations.

The Gillum firm's last documented check of the modified final design — so-called "shop drawings" prepared by Havens' employees — was signed off by Gillum employee Edward C. Jantosik, a non-engineer who had once failed the state's written engineering exam. Later, at the engineers' state license hearings in 1984, Jantosik testified that he periodically discussed design questions with Duncan but did not know himself how to go about mathematically checking the safety of such steel connections. "I leave that up to the engineers," he testified.

The engineers' principal defense was that it had been a standard industry practice for years for engineers to delegate various design tasks and checks to specialty firms like Havens. No single engineering firm, they argued, can hope to check — nor can it financially afford to check — every connection, weld and other design detail.

"We're not in the position to review shop drawings by checking every single element, every little nut, washers, weld, that the (steel) fabricator is putting on the job," Duncan would later testify. "We do not have the responsibility."

Almost two decades later, in a 2000 article on the skywalks collapse for the professional journal Forensic Engineering, Gillum continued to argue that point.

But in the article Gillum made an unexpected observation: "Proper engineering takes time to provide proper oversight and overloaded engineers, draftsman and project managers are susceptible and prone to making mistakes. *Dan Duncan had many projects to manage and much of my time was spent traveling and out of the office.*" (The italicized emphasis is Gillum's.)

Later in the same article Gillum urged design professionals to "Take the time to check your own work! Do not assume someone else will … Overall responsibility should not be delegated … *The buck*

TONY RINELLA

Tony Rinella and some other members of the Fine Arts Singles in Kansas City were regulars at the Friday night tea dance at the Hyatt. On the evening of July 17, Rinella was out on the floor dancing with a woman he met through a mutual friend. But he did not want to enter the dance contest that started at 7 p.m.

"She pleaded with me, 'Would you get in the dance contest with me?' " Rinella said. "So we registered and got the number 13." He wasn't superstitious and declined to trade it for another one.

"We got out on the dance floor and we were struttin' our stuff when all of a sudden I hear this crashing sound," Rinella said. "I looked up and there were people falling off the top balcony."

As the skywalks came down, Rinella grabbed his dance partner by the hand and they dove for safety toward the escalator. The skywalks landed on people in line for a drink and spectators along the front windows. One of those killed was a friend of Rinella's, Vernon Mitchell, who was in the drink line.

Agreeing to dance in the contest probably saved his life, Rinella said.

"If she had never asked me to dance, I would have been in line at the bar area," Rinella said.

Todd Feeback, The Star

stops with the Engineer of Record."

Havens consistently made that same argument throughout years of legal action; final responsibility rests with the engineers.

Judge Deutsch agreed with Havens and with state laws that framed and spelled out engineers' design responsibilities. In his ruling the judge concluded that the Gillum engineers' delegation of that responsibility "smacks of cost/benefit analysis run amok … and leaves the owner and public unprotected from a hazardous activity for no greater purpose than their own convenience and financial benefit."

Under the engineers' original design and the steel company's modified connection scheme, support rods were to pass through the center of the skywalks' 8-inch hanger box beams. These beams were founded by welding two C-shaped steel pieces together, toe-to-toe (like this: "[]"), to form the box. In each case the greatest stresses were placed directly on those welded joints.

Along the way someone realized that to hang both the fourth- and second-floor skywalks from the same ceiling rods, joined by simple nut and washer connections, would require that each hanger rod be threaded along much of its three-story length to allow both the lower and upper nuts to be threaded into place. That, however, would have made handling and installation of the rods and the walkways' concrete slabs infinitely more difficult and would have placed the rods at risk of serious thread damage.

The fateful design change determined that the fourth-floor box beams would be hung from the ceiling via six rods, as originally designed by the architect and the engineers. The second-floor walkway was to hang directly below, also as originally designed. But instead of hanging from the same six ceiling rods, it would be hung by a separate set of rods attached to the fourth-floor box beams, offset four inches from the ceiling rods.

In effect, the change doubled the weight and stress on the fourth-floor box beams.

As engineers Piotr D. Moncarz and Robert K. Taylor summed it up in the May 2000 issue of the Journal of Performance of Constructed Facilities, "The collapse occurred simply because of the doubling of the load on the connection resulting from an ill-considered change of an ill-defined structural

Engineer Richard Marshall of the National Bureau of Standards attached a jack to the underside of a section of the skywalks as he prepared to weigh it.

Kansas City Star/Times

FIVE TRAUMATIC YEARS FOR THE CITY

The collapse of the skywalks at the Hyatt Regency added another grim link to the chain of cataclysms that plagued the city in the late 1970s and early 1980s.

Sept. 12, 1977 Brush Creek flash flood devastates the Country Club Plaza and takes 25 lives.

Jan. 28, 1978 20 people die in an early morning four-alarm fire at the Coates House, at 10th Street in downtown.

June 4, 1979 Roof of Kemper Arena caves in from high winds and torrential rain, causing $5.1 million in damage.

In July 1980 A heat wave bakes the city, causing 157 deaths, most of them elderly.

April 1981 Eight people die in a fire at the Westport Central Apartments in the city's worst arson-homicide.

Source: The Kansas City Star

Engineers Richard Marshall and Edgar Leyendecker of the National Bureau of Standards helped establish the weight of each skywalk at more than 35 tons.

detail."

Survivors reported hearing a loud crack or bang just before the sky-walks fell. That noise almost certainly was the initial nut and washer connection failing and slamming through the welded box beam joint, shredding steel like a staple being pulled through a piece of paper. With no backup or redundant support system that initial failure immediately overloaded the remaining connections and the whole assembly came crashing down.

Experts have long agreed that the double-rod design might have worked with a few simple modifications. One option would have joined the C-channel beams back-to-back (like this: "][")), rather than the toe-to-toe ("[]") configuration that was used. They also say the use of larger washers or thick steel plates functioning as washers would have spread the stresses to the box beams' stronger vertical walls.

Kansas City area engineer Wayne G. Lischka, who played a pivotal role in 1981 in analyzing aspects of the collapse as a technical consultant to The Kansas City Star, said 12 small steel plates might have prevented the collapse, and they could have been purchased at the time for about $1 apiece.

Lischka's role was a groundbreaking one for Kansas City journalism. Never before had a news organization here so readily engaged an expert, nor depended so heavily on one to filter, shape and become part of its news coverage.

Then a 32-year-old engineer still building his suburban Kansas City practice, Lischka was not the newspaper's first choice for the job. But he was the first to accept the challenge declined by others fearful, perhaps, to speak out about their own professional community's role in a deadly structural failure inside Kansas City's newest architectural jewel, a jewel owned by one of the city's most beloved corporate citizens, Hallmark Cards.

Such fears were real. Lischka says there are engineering firms in town that still today refuse to work with him.

"I knew there would be some people who would criticize me, but I felt it was morally the right thing to do," he said.

Lischka was issued press credentials Monday morning after the collapse and remained at the side of reporters and editors on and off

"The collapse occurred simply because of the doubling of the load on the connection resulting from an ill-considered change of an ill-defined structural detail."

Engineers Piotr D. Moncarz and Robert K. Taylor,
in an article in the Journal of Performance
of Constructed Facilities, May 2000

ORIGINAL DESIGN

Six single-rod assemblies, secured to steel beams in the ceiling, were to run continuously through the skywalk box beams on the fourth floor to the box beams on the second-floor skywalk.

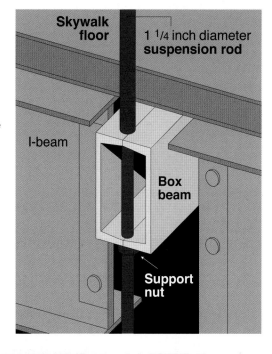

Skywalk floor

1 1/4 inch diameter suspension rod

I-beam

Box beam

Support nut

ALTERED DESIGN

What the architects called for was altered to facilitate construction. The change, however, doubled the stress on the fourth-floor box beams.

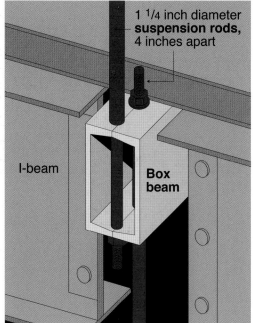

1 1/4 inch diameter suspension rods, 4 inches apart

I-beam

Box beam

Dave Eames, The Star

for months. He was quickly put to work that same morning when officials opened the atrium for tightly restricted press access and photography from a second-floor terrace overlooking the lobby but more than 50 feet away from the skywalk wreckage.

By then Star reporter Thomas G. Watts had already heavily worked a source that he has steadfastly declined to reveal to this day. That "deep throat" source he first encountered in the hotel lobby the night of the collapse possessed extraordinary knowledge of Hyatt construction details and had pointed the newspaper, thus Lischka, to focus on the rod-to-box beam connections. Those connections, of course, were the logical first place to look anyway.

That Monday morning in the hotel lobby Lischka eyeballed the connections himself, and later studied close-up photos captured by telescopic lens. That evening city officials granted The Star rare after-hours access to its file of Hyatt blueprints and other building records.

Lischka, reporter Steve Kaut and I shuffled through boxes of documents in a tiny, vacant office inside a nearly deserted City Hall, until shortly after 6 p.m. when Lischka had his "eureka" moment.

"I think these plans are different than what was actually constructed," he said.

The next day the news story, along with photos and detailed drawings of the modified design and how it failed, topped Page 1 in The Star. The headline, "Critical design change is linked to collapse of Hyatt's sky walks," blared from airport news boxes and greeted the National Bureau of Standards investigative team that arrived in town that day to begin its probe of the collapse.

The bureau's 256-page report, with exhaustive technical detail, was issued in February 1982. Its findings only echoed and amplified Lischka's first-day-on-the-job conclusions.

It concluded, "With this change in hanger rod arrangement, the ultimate capacity of the walkways was so significantly reduced that, from the day of construction, they had only minimal capacity to resist their own weight and had virtually no capacity to resist additional loads imposed by people."

According to the bureau's analysis of video shot in the packed lobby just minutes before the collapse by a television news crew cover-

Lischka worked alongside reporter Rick Alm and others, poring over documents and studying photographic evidence and drawings.

"It was pitch black, but all of a sudden I saw a sliver of light."

KATHY MORTON

Aaron Leimkuehler, The Star

Kathy Morton was at the Hyatt for a birthday gathering. Morton and a friend decided to stay a while and watch the dance. Morton, 24 at the time, lived in Belton and worked downtown.

Morton and her friend were near the staircase on the main level, "when all of a sudden there was a big crash."

The collapse knocked the two of them to the floor, but they ended up in a small cavity between the skywalks, her friend's ankles were under Morton's body.

"I was lying on my stomach, and it was pitch black," Morton said. "A man's leg was under my stomach."

Morton could lift her arms and head but not much. She had fractured a small part of her pelvis, broken her leg and cut her foot.

"I was freaking out, we were screaming," Morton said. "I thought the whole hotel had collapsed."

Realizing there was little more they could do, the women calmed down and started to say the Lord's Prayer. Then, they felt liquid running beneath their bodies and thought it was blood. It was actually water from the burst pipe, but it was mixing with blood as it passed by.

They could then hear the voices of rescue workers yelling. They yelled back, were located and rescued about an hour later when part of the fourth-floor skywalk was moved off to the side.

"It was pitch black, but all of a sudden I saw a sliver of light," Morton said. Her friend was taken to a nearby hospital, and Morton was airlifted to Kansas University Medical Center, which she described as a scary experience all by itself.

She can't help but think how a small space in the collapsed skywalks saved her life and her friend's. "Obviously we were very lucky," she said.

ing the hotel's tea dance, 63 people were estimated to be standing on the walkways when they fell, including 56 on the second-floor level.

MISSED WARNING SIGNS

In hindsight it is still stunning that there were so many chances to catch and correct the fatal design error.

During construction on Oct. 14, 1979, about 20 percent of the hotel's atrium roof collapsed. The ensuing investigation of that failure found dozens of bad connections in the roof and elsewhere in the atrium's steel skeleton.

Corrective work led to an overhaul of the skywalk spans' connections to the atrium walls. But no record has ever surfaced that suggests any of the rod-to-box beam connections were examined.

In the aftermath of the roof collapse, Hallmark President Donald J. Hall, according to the minutes of a meeting with construction team executives, insisted that extraordinary efforts be made to ensure the entire building's safety. At that same meeting engineer Jack Gillum assured those present that "every connection in the atrium, both steel-to-steel and steel-to-concrete" had been reviewed.

Later under oath at his deposition hearing Duncan, the projects' chief engineer, contradicted that assertion by Gillum. "I don't know of anyone who did that," he testified.

Just weeks after the roof collapse in 1979, Duncan himself verified the safety of the skywalks in a written report to the hotel owners. "We then checked the suspended bridges and found them to be satisfactory," he wrote.

Such inconsistencies in the written record and the engineers' defense arguments weighed heavily on Deutsch who, in his ruling, termed them "worse than unacceptable and constituted a fraud upon the owner and architect."

The only acknowledgement by anyone that they looked specifically at the nut-and-washer-to-box beam connections after the skywalks were erected in mid-August 1979 came during the deposition of Daniel H. Hafley, who was just 20 when he was hired on to his first-ever construction industry job by Hyatt subcontractor General

Kansas City Star/Times

In their search for clues, investigators examined likely areas of failure, including the place where the skywalks had pulled away from the wall.

67

There were still other warning signs that, in hindsight, suggest the inexorable process of steel deformation and the inevitable collapse was well under way and easily detectable, had anyone looked.

Inspector James Stratta, the California engineer who had determined the cause of the Kemper Arena roof collapse two years earlier, was back in Kansas City for another structural failure. In August, as workmen carried out one of the rods that held up the fourth-floor skywalk, Stratta kept his eyes on the ceiling where the other support rods were being removed.

68

Testing, an on-site material testing and inspection service.

Under oath Hafley said none of his superiors had ever instructed him to examine the critical hanger connections. But he testified that he did once look at them to determine whether the nuts and washers were in place as designed. By that time the National Bureau of Standards experts agreed that some deflection or bending in the stressed steel box beams would have been obvious — to a trained observer.

There were still other warning signs that, in hindsight, suggest the inexorable process of steel deformation and the inevitable collapse was well under way and easily detectable, had anyone looked.

Just weeks before the hotel opened in July 1980 a construction worker on May 9 reported that the walkways appeared to be "sagging" about 3/4ths of an inch.

That concern was passed on to the hotel architects' on-site representative, Jerome W. Sifers, who confirmed the sagging and documented it as "quite evident" in a routine daily report. But he later testified that he never pursued the matter with his superiors or any other construction team members.

Similar sagging was noted after the hotel opened when another worker made a visual alignment of the skywalk handrails and reported they appeared to be uneven. That problem was noted on an Aug. 15, 1980, checklist of about 130 then still-pending construction issues at the hotel. "Why isn't (hand) rail height (on the skywalks) the same?" it asked. There was no further mention of the problem in scores of subsequent checklists.

The last chance to find and correct the design flaw appeared to come in February 1981 while checklist work was still under way seven months after the hotel had opened. Drywall worker John E. Holmes noticed "a slight curvature" or bending in the skywalks' fourth-floor box beams while he was encasing them behind drywall. Holmes, who recounted his observation in a 1982 interview with The Star, said he never reported the matter because he believed at the time that some bending in steel was normal.

Such tragic missed opportunities were lamented by Edward O. Pfrang who headed the federal government skywalk probe as chief of the structures division of the National Bureau of Standards.

In 1982, he told the newspapers' Hyatt Papers reporting team that the box beams "almost certainly" began to deform as soon as the full weight of the skywalks was placed on them.

"By the time they finished construction ... that connection almost certainly was distorted to the point that if someone had been looking for it or if a trained person had looked at it, he would have seen there were clear signs of distress."

Berkebile, the hotel's principal architect, blames the collapse on "human error, no question."

"I never will know what actually happened," he said. "I don't think anyone ever looked at that (connection) design."

What Berkebile is certain of today remains unchanged from the day he conceived the notion of skywalks soaring across the atrium lobby: "That bridge was not a risky thing," he said.

"It should have been a routine connection."

In the years following the Hyatt tragedy, Gillum, a 1950 graduate in architectural engineering from the University of Kansas, wrote and spoke publicly about the collapse.

Edward Pfrang led the federal investigation of the skywalks collapse.

In a 20th anniversary interview with The Star, he said the reason he speaks publicly about the Hyatt tragedy is because "engineering societies need to talk about failures ... scare the daylights" out of other engineers so they understand how mistakes can so easily slip by.

"This is a tragedy I think about 365 days a year," he said. "I think

Jennifer Sheeley Chapin

I was 26 at the time of this disaster.
… (We) were having dinner at the
Terrace Restaurant. I wanted to be
on the skywalk and was waiting for
my friend, Dean, to finish his eighth
cup of coffee. It was the
"ping, ping" I heard first.
Then I saw the skywalks start to
drop. The collective gasps of the
people I'll never forget. I turned
away from the sight and buried my
head in Dean's chest and screamed
"God, God, oh God!" Passing by
the entry to where the first walkway
had been, I decided to not hear. I
didn't want to hear the cries of the
injured or the grieved. Everything
went silent.

about it anytime I walk into a public building."

For several years beginning in 1999 Gillum was an adjunct professor of civil engineering at Washington University in St. Louis where he lectured to engineering seniors and graduate students. A 2005 course description for one of his classes noted: "The student will gain an insight into success's (sic) and failures of the real world of design and construction."

In one version of his public remarks prepared for a 2004 management conference in Kansas City that can be found online, Gillum insisted that neither he nor any of his engineers were alerted to any of the red flags that were raised about the skywalks. His power point slides outlined numerous aspects of the collapse including one entitled, "What should have occurred?"

One of the bullet points: "Engineer notified of warnings!"

Paul Munger, who was chairman of the state licensing panel that stripped Gillum and Duncan of their Missouri licenses in 1986 and who still makes occasional public appearances to discuss the tragedy, said, "I know Jack. He's a good engineer … he means well. But Jack would never admit he made a mistake in the Hyatt."

The bottom line for Munger is this: "His seal is on the work: 114 people died."

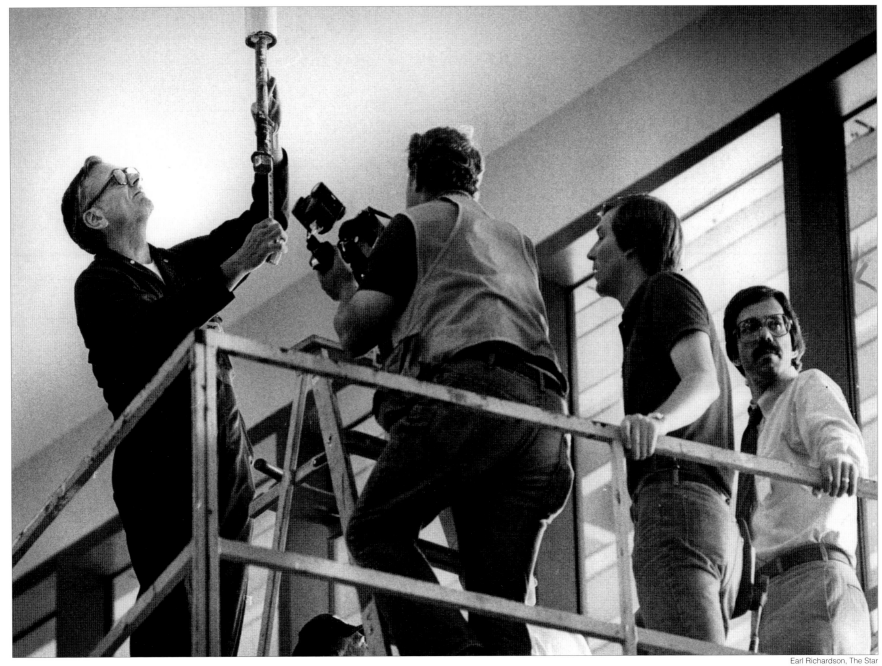

Before the ceiling rods were removed, inspectors took measurements and photographed them.

Television cameramen and print photographers shared space on the mezzanine level to shoot images. The day after the collapse, police liaison officers restricted members of the media to two areas inside the Hyatt from where they could record what they saw in the lobby below. But no audio was allowed.

Dan White, The Star

72

The angle from afar

Despite being kept at a distance, a Kansas City Star photographer used a telephoto lens to capture the images that would be used by engineer Wayne Lischka as he helped sleuth out the cause of the collapse.

The Kansas City Times

46 killed in Hyatt collapse

as tea dance turns to terror

REPORTING
THE STORY

Print, television and radio pulled out all the stops to cover the disaster.

By Carol Powers

*T*he collapse of the skywalks at the Hyatt Regency hotel was the biggest news story Kansas City had ever seen. It was front page news across the nation.

It killed 114 people, including 18 married couples, and it remains the deadliest building design failure in U.S. history. The rescue operation involved hundreds of people, took almost 13 hours and tested the city's emergency response and medical nfrastructure.

It was also a test of the readiness of KC media to explain to the public what happened and why.

■■■

The Kansas City Times newsroom was quiet and nearly empty. The Times was having its usual slow Friday. The Times sister paper, The Star, had published its final edition several

The Kansas City Times the next morning announced the tragedy in big bold type, citing the most accurate estimate of deaths at the time it went to press. Tragically, that estimate of deaths proved to be low.

Kansas City Star

hours earlier, and most of the staff had already scattered for the evening.

Tom Ramstack, a young Times reporter, was at his desk in the newsroom when he heard sirens. He didn't pay much attention until he saw assistant managing editor Monroe Dodd return to the newsroom from dinner at The Pub, across the street, and shout across the room for Ramstack to call the police and find out what was going on at Crown Center. He would be the first reporter dispatched from the newsroom to the scene.

At the Johnson County office at 75th and Antioch, bureau chief Bill Norton was routinely monitoring Johnson County police radios when he heard something odd. Kansas City dispatchers were calling for more ambulances. Norton picked up the phone and called downtown, eventually reaching police reporter Greg Reeves and assistant city editor Mike Zakoura.

The Star's softball team had won its first game of the season, by forfeit, early that evening and had repaired to The Bigger Jigger to celebrate. Among the players at the bar was Mike Waller, managing editor of The Star.

Mike Davies, editor of both the Star and Times, had just arrived at home and was about to sit down when the phone rang.

James Hale, publisher of both papers, was on the highway headed for a boating weekend in the Ozarks. There would be a message waiting for him at the marina.

Star reporter Rick Alm, city editor David Zeeck and Darryl Levings, an assistant city editor, had just finished dinner with their wives at the Hereford House downtown. On the way out of the restaurant, they noticed two women, very excited, at the pay phone in the foyer. They had what looked like blood on their clothes.

Levings asked them what had happened.

What they said was a gush of words, half remembered today, that left the journalists with one impression: Something catastrophic — a collapse of the ceiling, the roof, the hotel itself — had just happened at the Hyatt Regency.

Levings called Thomas G. Watts, one of the Star's senior writers. Then Levings, Zeeck and Alm piled into Alm's car, raided the glove compartment for notebooks and raced for the Hyatt.

■ ■ ■

Channel 9's Micheal Mahoney was the only reporter on the scene when the skywalks fell. He had been at KMBC for only a year, and although his background was hard news, he was on a feature assignment.

The weekly tea dances were airy affairs in the elegant, one-year-old hotel. Tea could be had, but orders at the bar ran more to harder stuff. That night hundreds of couples in evening wear were swaying to the music of the Steve Miller band in the atrium lobby. Dozens more were on the three skywalks.

Mahoney and cameraman Dave Forstate had just ridden up the escalator, away from the dance, to conduct some interviews. Mahoney was bent over, fishing in Forstate's bag for a fresh battery, when he heard a couple of sharp pings, like something metallic.

"I looked and saw the skywalk tear loose. It was like a reverse drawbridge. Instead of going up, it was going down. It started to break apart. I suppose I saw people falling, but

Aaron Leimkuehler, The Star

"I looked and saw the skywalk tear loose. I suppose I saw people falling, but that's not a vivid memory."

Micheal Mahoney,
television reporter, KMBC

Aaron Leimkuehler, The Star

"The concrete dust was rising ... saws were cranked up ... I can't say I heard anyone scream. I think I blocked a lot of it."

Darryl Levings,
then-assistant city editor, The Kansas City Star

that's not a vivid memory."

Mahoney found a phone in the kitchen and called for an outside line. "Good evening, Hyatt." The switchboard operator didn't yet know anything had happened.

After briefing his colleagues at the station, he and Forstate went back down to shoot what could only be described as carnage. A water pipe had burst and Mahoney, who had on rubber-soled shoes, didn't want to slip and damage the tape. The water on the floor was turning red with blood.

■ ■ ■

Levings, Alm and Zeeck got to the hotel just as the first emergency responders were showing up. They split up and sought different vantage points.

Alm stepped into the lobby. It took awhile for his eyes to adjust to the gloom and dust.

"There was a brief period — maybe a minute, maybe five — when I had a sense I was the only living thing in that lobby," he recalls. "There was an eerie silence. The only sound was the gushing of water from a broken main in the lobby's north wall. The dead were mostly unseen under the wreckage."

Levings took a fire escape up and popped out on the third floor, where he walked out onto the skywalk that hadn't failed. He saw clearly what had happened. Through a window he could see a bank clock across the street, and as he took notes he recorded the times, minute by minute. The Star would use that timeline to construct a story for the special section that wrapped Sunday's paper.

After a while, nonessential people, including reporters, were asked to leave, but Levings was among several reporters who managed to stay. He left the skywalk and found a different perch, behind a potted palm on the third floor.

For Levings, now The Star's foreign editor, some of what he witnessed remains a vivid memory.

"The concrete dust was rising, and the bodies, crushed

under tons of concrete and steel, were white. The saws were cranked up, adding blue smoke. Water was rushing out of a pipe that must have been running through one of the skywalks. The bodies of the dead were being dragged into a convention room. I can't say I heard anyone scream. I think I blocked a lot of it."

There was a police officer standing close to Levings at this point, and as they surveyed the carnage below, Levings asked him if he'd ever seen anything as horrific as this.

"Yeah," he said. " 'Nam."

■ ■ ■

At KCMO radio, Dan Verbeck was in the newsroom when he heard the calls for assistance. He was less than 10 minutes away.

"I was on I-35 and realized as I crossed the state line that Johnson County MedAct ambulances were passing me."

At the hotel, they hadn't yet closed the place off to reporters, and he walked across the remaining third-floor skywalk with Police Chief Norman A. Caron.

He had inadvertently left his tape recorder on and would later listen to the sounds of people calling for help, people in anguish. Blood has a distinctive odor, he says.

"Multiply that by the number of people who were bleeding. It's the sort of thing you never mention on the air; it would offend people and serve no purpose."

Verbeck, now a reporter at KCUR, initially used a two-way radio and portable hookup, and when he first called the station, a new technician kept disconnecting him. "I couldn't get the story on for about five minutes. By this time there were firefighters on the east side of the building knocking out windows with axes. The rescue became the story."

He watched as rescue workers wormed their way into cramped spaces to reach people who were trapped. Doctors sedated some of them. There were amputations to get some of them out.

"I never used any of this on the air," Verbeck says. "It was hard to listen to."

He would be at the scene until 5 a.m. Saturday. Anchor Noel Heckerson "would ask me questions to keep me on track, because I was getting punchy."

The reporter, who was in his 30s at the time, has two other clear memories.

The waiters in the garden restaurant on the mezzanine "had taken off their starched jackets and were putting them around people's shoulders. The lowest-paid people in the place."

He still has the shoes he wore that night. "I thought, I can't throw away a pair of Florsheim wingtips. But I never wore them again. My pants were pink up to the knees."

■ ■ ■

Walt Bodine, even then the dean of Kansas City radio news, was visiting family friends when he got the call. Bodine and KMBZ news director Rod Allen started with short broadcasts and went full time to the story at 9:30 p.m. They were on the air until 6 a.m., mixing reports from four reporters at the scene with on-air phone calls from medical and emergency personnel and people who'd been at the tea dance.

In the studio at KCMO-TV, anchors Wendall Anschutz and Steve Dawson were taking feeds from Channel 5 reporter Barney McCoy. The station alternated that with footage from Truman Medical Center and film from inside the hotel showing a priest attending to the living and giving last rites.

Scott Feldman, one of KMBC-TV's two anchors, decided to leave the studio near Swope Park to do interviews at the scene. WDAF also sent one of its anchors, Stacy Smith, to the hotel. All three TV stations broadcast repeated appeals for blood.

City editor David Zeeck (standing at top left) led a meeting of The Kansas City Star staff the day after the collapse.

Once he got back to the Star, Waller writes in his new book "Blood on the Out-Basket: Lessons in Leadership from a Newspaper Junkie," it became clear that to get to the bottom of what went wrong, the paper needed expert help.

"I knew that no matter that the Halls were good people, everybody would circle the wagons," he says.

The staff was divided into teams, with Zeeck, now president and publisher of the Tacoma News-Tribune, directing the coverage. Waller, the managing editor, asked the Levings team to find a structural engineer who was willing to confirm on the record what the paper found. It was a pivotal decision. Ultimately, each paper hired an engineer.

Reporter Robert Trussell, now The Star's theater critic, had been sent to hospital emergency rooms to report on the delivery of victims. He returned to the newsroom. At one point that night, Trussell remembers, Waller yelled, "I want to find out who built the fucking thing!"

It was about 9:30 p.m. when Davies, the papers' editor, called Hale on his boat in the Ozarks. He warned that in the coming weeks the papers' cost for newsprint and overtime would be monumental.

The publisher's response: "I don't care what it costs, just do it right."

The morning Times and afternoon Star staffs were not normally in the building at the same time. They usually worked separate 12-hour shifts but used the same desks, phones, copiers and library. And they were very competitive.

"It was like two scorpions in a bottle," Levings recalls.

And that night nearly everyone from both staffs was called in.

In the days to come, Levings remembers, Davies would come through the newsroom and use that rivalry to advantage.

"He'd go to The Times editors and say something like, 'That's a really good angle you've got on that, but I've got to tell you The Star's ahead of you.' Then he'd stop by The Star

Star photographer Talis Bergmanis was stopped outside the Hyatt Regency by a security guard. After the initial evening, the media was kept outside the perimeter for the most part.

Facing page: Assistant city editor Steve Paul and reporter Greg Edwards let their cigarettes wait as they worked on a story for the Sunday edition.

Polishing the story

"A gray sky rained tears Saturday on a city overcome with grief." So began The Kansas City Star's Page 1 story on the Sunday following the disaster.

At left, reporter Diane Stafford sat at the keyboard as that story came together under the watchful eyes of reporter Steve Woodward (standing), assistant city editor Steve Paul (left) and Johnson County bureau chief Bill Norton.

At right, city editor David Zeeck (seated), copy editor Mike Miller (right) and reporter Roy Wenzl discussed a different story for the same edition.

Kansas City Star photos

desk and say, 'That was a great story yesterday, but you might want to check out such and such a development. I hear The Times is all over it.' "

But Friday night, July 17, belonged to The Times. Assistant managing editors Dodd and Steve Shirk were in charge.

Shirk wanted an illustration from inside the Hyatt. Tom Dolphens, a new staff artist, and the more experienced Gayland Burke went to the hotel, where Burke sketched inside the lobby for almost an hour.

Back in the newspaper's art department he finished a large graphic of the damaged hotel lobby using his sketches and file slides provided by Marty Petty, the assistant managing editor for art and design for both papers. Her ongoing supervision of the visuals for the coverage didn't hurt her career. She later went to the Hartford Courant where she was named publisher in 1997, then the St. Petersburg Times where she was executive vice president and then publisher.

Assistant city editor Mike DeArmond, now a sports reporter at The Star, sat down and wrote the main story from everyone's feeds, and working against the clock, The Times produced five full extra pages on the disaster by the final edition.

Several people recall a peculiar incident that involved a young Times medical writer. Davies had sent him to the Hyatt to help cover the rescue efforts. Several editors were thinking his story might run on Page 1. When the reporter came back, he said he didn't think there was a story there. Davies overheard it and "went crazy." Some time later, the reporter was gone.

"In retrospect," Waller says, "no reporter would do that. He had to have been in shock."

■ ■ ■

Channel 9's Mahoney and Forstate went back to the station and did a segment on the 10 o'clock news. Mahoney appeared that night on "Nightline" with Ted Koppel. He stayed with the story for months afterwards, winning the Mall Dodson National Headliners Award for continued coverage. He wishes it had been a different kind of story, "but the whole episode helped make my career in Kansas City, no question."

On Tuesday, The Star had a story about the structural design flaw that caused the accident stripped across the top of Page 1. It was written by Alm and Watts.

The newspaper executive who probably took the most pressure that week and in the months to come was Hale.

It wasn't much of a stretch to say Hallmark Cards was the most popular company in town, and many business leaders came to believe that the constant coverage was giving the city a black eye. They put pressure on the newspaper, and some of them took their complaints to New York, to the CEO and president of Capital Cities Inc., the papers' corporate owners.

But Hale never caved.

"It was his finest hour," Levings says. "If there was a finer one, I don't know what it was."

In April 1982, The Star and Times were jointly awarded the Pulitzer Prize for their coverage of the Hyatt disaster and the investigation of its cause. In May of that year, the National Bureau of Standards issued its report on the collapse. It sustained the papers' conclusions that a minor design change had been made that doubled the stress at critical connecting points on the second- and fourth-floor skywalks. It went further, finding that even the original design would not have met the standards of the Kansas City building code.

In the weeks after the collapse, a handful of Star and Times people sought psychological help, Waller says. "The paper paid for it and gave them time off."

— *Joe Popper contributed to this story.*

Members of the art staff — Tom Strongman (from left), art director Marty Petty and photographers Jim McTaggart and Talis Bergmanis — discussed the story's presentation.

Mike Davies, editor of both
The Times and The Star,
frequently played the
competing staffs against
each other, goading one to
top the other and vice versa.
He warned the papers'

Mike Davies

publisher, Jim Hale, that in the coming weeks the cost of newsprint and overtime would be monumental. Hale's response: "I don't care what it costs, just do it right."

Jim Hale

"People saw my black shoes sticking out from the debris and pulled me out. Two or three rescue workers carried me out on a serving tray."

SOL AND ROSETTE KOENIGSBERG

Todd Feeback, The Star

S ol and Rosette Koenigsberg had been invited to dinner with some friends and decided to stop at the Hyatt on the way. They heard the dance contest being announced in the lobby and stayed a moment to watch, standing beneath the edge of the second-level skywalk.

When the skywalk came crashing down, Sol Koenigsberg was knocked to the ground by debris but apparently avoided a direct hit from the skywalk itself.

"The debris formed a pocket around my wife and she was able to crawl out behind someone who had already found their way through," Koenigsberg said. But Koenigsberg had been struck hard on the back and was buried under the debris and "everything went black," he said.

"Most people around me were killed instantly," Koenigsberg said. "People saw my black shoes sticking out from the debris and pulled me out. Two or three rescue workers carried me out on a serving tray."

Rosette Koenigsberg, though not seriously hurt, went into shock and became immobilized, he said. A photograph of the couple holding hands as they waited for medical attention appeared in Sunday's Kansas City Star.

Sol Koenigsberg suffered a broken back, crushed leg and internal injuries and was told he would always walk with a limp, but he eventually recovered completely.

In the hospital, 24 hours after the collapse, Koenigsberg had a flashback to his World War II days in the Pacific.

"I was back on my ship off Okinawa, and we were under attack by kamikaze pilots," Koenigsberg said. "One hit our ship and I was there."

Hospital attendants saw that he was rattled and calmed him down after about 15 or 20 minutes, he said.

"That is the only time I reacted like that," he said.

THEY WERE THERE

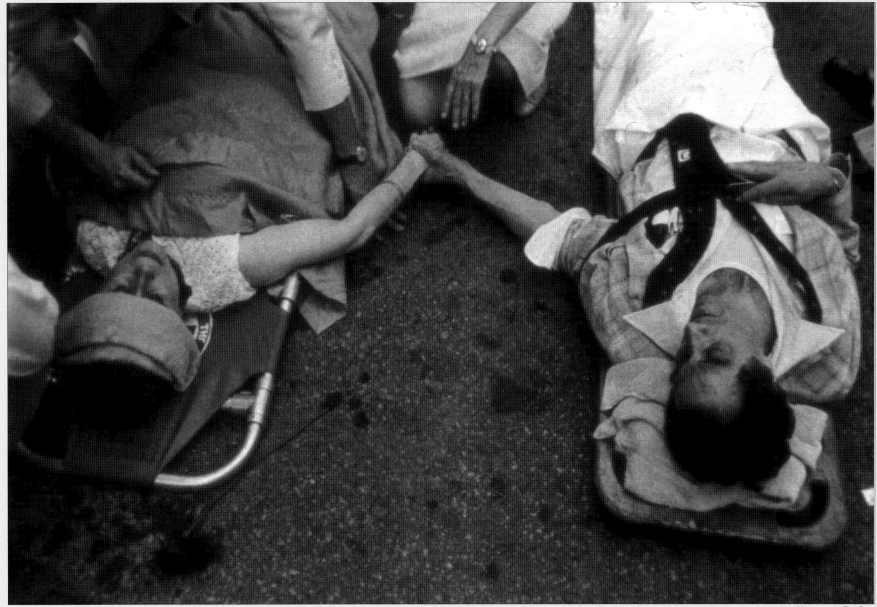

As they waited for medical attention outside the Hyatt Regency, Rosette and Sol Koenigsberg held hands and comforted each other. This photograph appeared in The Kansas City Star on Sunday, July 19, 1981.

Managing editor Mike Waller's decision to hire a structural engineer to work with The Star's staff proved pivotal in discovering the cause of the disaster. Both The Star and The Times were awarded the Pulitzer Prize, the news industry's highest award, for their coverage.

Kansas City Star

CHAPTER 4

LESSONS LEARNED

Part 1: Engineering a New Way

The tragedy brought tighter regulations, more oversight and higher standards to the industry.

By Rick Alm

Kansas City structural engineer Thomas F. Heausler had just graduated from Tulane University with an engineering degree when the skywalks fell in 1981.

The tragedy has played an outsized role in his professional life, and it has had a lasting effect on the entire field of engineering.

"It wasn't just a Kansas City event," he said. "The world has ended up a better place in the wake of the Hyatt collapse disaster."

The skywalks fell because "people weren't paying attention to the details," he said. Today they do. Preventing avoidable errors like the skywalks is ingrained in every engineer's educational DNA, if for no other reason than self-defense. "The engineers' responsibility," he said, "is to not be on the front page of the newspaper."

Emerging from the public relations rubble of the skywalks collapse, the nation's shell-shocked design and construction industries began to patch holes in standard procedures and practices that, in hindsight,

A flag at the Kansas City Fire Department's Alarm Exchange Building, at 22nd Street and Gillham Road, fluttered at half-staff as a tribute to those who died. The Exchange Building was the nerve center for emergency response during the emergency. The flag also flew for Fire Battalion Chief John Tvedten, who was off duty when he died at the hotel.

Mark Hinojosa, The Star

had allowed such an obviously flawed structure to be built.

There was no shortage of fault to be passed around. After the collapse, for instance, it was learned that Kansas City building inspectors had spent less than 19 hours checking the structural integrity of the 40-story hotel complex. Along the way numerous fire code violations also were discovered.

The fatal design change in the skywalks' steel support system was never reported to city engineers for their review. At the time, city officials said, there was no requirement for such changes to be reported. There are today.

A congressional committee that investigated the Hyatt and other structural failures in 1982 led to a national call for tightened standards on engineers' design responsibilities. Bill Quatman, an architect and a lawyer who was involved in some of the Hyatt litigation during the 1980s, said Kansas City was one of many cities that responded with tougher local building codes. Now, special inspections of steel connections and many other design elements are required, with particular attention given to anything built "in the field" that does not match design plans and drawings filed with the city.

Around the country, local and national building codes, professional standards and ethics, and education curricula all were drawn tighter in the aftermath of the Hyatt tragedy to clarify professional design responsibilities, liabilities and relationships and to ensure that proper

Robert Berkebile

"Human error can still happen. But today it's far less likely."

Robert J. Berkebile,
principal architect of BNIM

—————

"It comes down to integrity and everyone doing their job."

Bill Quatman,
architect and lawyer

Bill Quatman

design checks and construction inspections take place.

"We're all working today with better design tools, better communication," said Robert J. Berkebile, the principal architect who headed the consortium that designed the Hyatt. Today Berkebile is the principal at BNIM Architects Inc. in Kansas City.

In the years after the Hyatt collapse, Berkebile has turned to the study of public health and safety in architecture, searching for ways to improve both the product and the quality of human life, and BNIM has developed an international reputation with its work in sustainable architecture and environmentally friendly green design.

Driving him was the indelible memory of the Hyatt tragedy. "We were trying to do something for our community, and it ended up a tragedy."

Despite stronger building codes and stricter building standards today, Berkebile said, there still are no guarantees. "Human error can still happen. But today it's far less likely."

Over the past decade or so the advent and refinement of computerized modeling allow architects and engineers to build and "test drive" their designs and connections as the computer does the necessary calculations to analyze the materials involved and the stresses and loads in play.

Computer assisted design, however, is not without risk.

"We put a lot of faith in that," said Quatman. "We don't go back and do a back check on the computer's calculations."

While Quatman said he's never heard of a structural failure blamed on computer error, he concedes it could happen. "It comes down to integrity and everyone doing their job," he said. "If not, then sure, we can have another collapse."

Wayne Lischka agrees.

Lischka, who played a pivotal role in determining the design and technical causes of the skywalks collapse in 1981, applauds the virtues of computer-assisted engineering. But he cautions that technology can breed its own brand of errors.

"When you drew the details yourself in the past, you gave it some thought, and it was checked by someone with more expe-

"When you are under deadline issues, it is easy to miss things and pass over things that look good. All occupations have times when individuals are under pressure and do not think clearly."

Wayne Lischka,
Kansas City engineer

Wayne Lischka

rience," he said. "Today you do not have to think and, because it is computer generated, it is not always checked.

"When you are under deadline issues, it is easy to miss things and pass over things that look good. All occupations have times when individuals are under pressure and do not think clearly. This does not mean it is the software's problem. The problem is that we are having to think less and less, so we don't."

The architects, engineers and steel fabricators who designed and built the skywalks have long disputed whose job it was to perform the necessary mathematical calculations on the key connections that failed. As it turned out, no one did it. Yet, everyone put their stamp of approval on the design drawings.

Today the general counsel at Burns & McDonnell Engineering Co. in Kansas City and a key adviser to the Skywalk Memorial Foundation Inc., Quatman has been on the speaker's circuit for years recounting for audiences of professionals and laymen how the skywalk design process went so wrong and how public policy makers and the various design industries responded with reforms.

Another Hyatt figure also on the lecture circuit today is Paul Munger, chairman of the state licensing panel that stripped the Hyatt engineers and their firm of their Missouri licenses in 1986. Today he is chairman of the Professional Conduct Committee of the American Society of Civil Engineers.

"A lot of young people today are awed" by the Hyatt collapse, he said. "They don't think these kinds of things can happen."

The lesson he said he emphasizes to students and young engineers is "be conscientious … don't get too busy to pay attention to the details."

"There will be people who want you to cut corners," Munger said he warns young engineers. "Learn to say no. You can't cut corners. Public safety is always a part of our work product."

Munger said the Hyatt tragedy taught the design industry some painful lessons. "And I think we're still learning. You don't learn lessons from things that don't fall."

Thirty years after the Hyatt tragedy, Quatman said, a lot of the detailed connection work is still designed by the steel fabricators. "Engineers say we still don't design complex connections," he said.

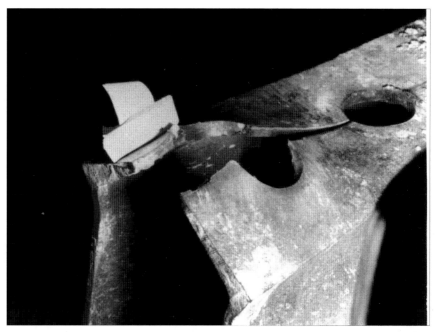

The box beam from the fourth floor split down the welded seam as the suspension rod pulled through.

"We rely on the steel fabricator. They're better at it."

Quatman is a critic of his own architectural fraternity, which responded to the Hyatt tragedy in the late '80s with a revision of its professional guidelines that added extensive disclaimer language — "weasel words," he calls them — to better insulate architects from responsibility after approving shop drawings and other elements designed by others.

Quatman adds that other professions and many individual companies similarly rewrote the language on their approval stamps and seals, which also attempts to split hairs on the extent and precise meaning of their review and approval of various design documents. Quatman contends such qualifying language would offer little if any legal cover in a courtroom.

"At the end of the day somebody has to put their seal on the documents," said Quatman. "You can delegate the work but not the responsibility. The buck stops there."

The reopening

The Hyatt Regency hotel reopened on Oct. 1, 1981, two and a half months after the disaster. Workmen, facing page, place flowers on the new second-floor walkway before the first guests, above, arrived. And providing entertainment for the new guests was Steve Miller at the piano. Miller and his big band were playing at the tea dance when the skywalks fell.

99

Part 2: Responding to Catastrophe

What the skywalks collapse taught us about dealing with major disasters

By Kevin Murphy

Without doubt, the skywalks collapse caught the Kansas City emergency response community unprepared. But how could anyone have foreseen a catastrophe of this dimension?

An unprecedented task awaited firefighters as they arrived to find hundreds of people dead or injured, many of them trapped.

"We were trained for structural collapses, but the magnitude of this event was overwhelming," said Charley Fisher, deputy chief of the Kansas City Fire Department at the time.

By and large, the fire, police, medical personnel and other rescue workers won praise for their work, but they knew there was much room for improvement.

The Hyatt disaster became a learning ground for how to plan and execute a rescue operation. Not only here, but across the nation. It led to changes in training, organizing and equipping rescue workers and broke new ground in the treatment of post-traumatic stress disorder.

Fisher and other Kansas City fire, police and emergency medical professionals traveled the country giving seminars and training sessions on lessons learned at the Hyatt disaster. Fisher, who retired as chief of the department in 1996, still

"Our whole region is better prepared for every emergency and disaster than we ever were before."

Smokey Dyer, KCMO fire chief

conducts seminars today.

Meanwhile, an infusion of federal Homeland Security funds after the Sept. 11, 2001, terrorist attacks helped Kansas City and other communities prepare for virtually any type of accidental, natural or man-made disaster, said Smokey Dyer, chief of the Kansas City Fire Department.

"Our whole region is better prepared for every emergency and disaster than we ever were before," Dyer said.

Some of that basic preparation dates back to the events of July 17, 1981.

One of the first lessons learned from that catastrophe was that some police, fire and other rescue personnel parked too close to the scene, in cars and vehicles not needed for the rescue operation. Unattended vehicles hampered access to the hotel by ambulances or other critical equipment. Tow trucks had to remove some vehicles, Fisher said.

The solution: staging areas a block or more away for nonessential vehicles to park. Police officers, firefighters and others can walk to the disaster site or get dropped off if they have equipment to carry. Staging is now a common procedure.

Inside the Hyatt that night, early responders tended to want to help every injured person who cried out, officials said later. That could work to the detriment of helping the most seriously hurt people first in an orderly fashion, said Ron Palmer, a Kansas City police captain and Central Patrol Division commander who was at the Hyatt that night.

"You can't get so focused on one individual that you ignore the larger picture," said Palmer, who now has a security consulting firm in Tulsa, Okla. "We had to secure that lobby and set up the larger response."

The Hyatt also spurred a more orderly system of keeping track of and identifying people who should have access to a disaster site and to what degree. Identification tags are commonplace now for emergency responders, the media and volunteers, such as Red Cross workers.

A police officer usually would be responsible for checking or issuing ID at a controlled access site. At the Hyatt, especially at first,

people got into the building who had no real purpose there, Palmer said.

"An ID system has become standard operating procedure because we couldn't tell who was who that night," Palmer said.

Handling the media also tightened in the wake of the Hyatt disaster. Authorities usually try to limit media access to scenes of disasters or major crimes, largely so that rescue workers or investigators can do their jobs without reporters asking questions of them and the victims.

In the first 20 minutes or so after the skywalks collapse, reporters had unfettered access to the building. Before long, they were asked to leave, and a staging area for the media was set up in front of the hotel. But that proved to interfere with access so it was moved farther away, to the north of the building.

Today, the media is sometimes kept well away from the scene of major events. Part of the reason is that television news crews today generally have large satellite trucks that take up space, Palmer said. A spokesperson for the command post usually gives updates at the media staging area.

Another common practice triggered by the Hyatt event is to set up a phone line dedicated to taking calls from relatives seeking information on potential victims. In order to respond to calls, someone is assigned to keep a roster of victims who have died, were treated or were transferred to a hospital.

"That all becomes part of the command post now," Palmer said.

The Hyatt disaster exposed other communications shortcomings. For instance, the media was told to spread the word that blood donors were needed, but that information did not go to the nearby Community Blood Center. Residents eager to help injured victims descended upon the blood bank, which was not ready to handle that many people.

After the disaster, officials made sure that blood banks were automatically notified at a time of potential multiple casualties, Fisher said.

At the Hyatt, rescue workers learned quickly that they lacked equipment needed to reach people trapped under the skywalks.

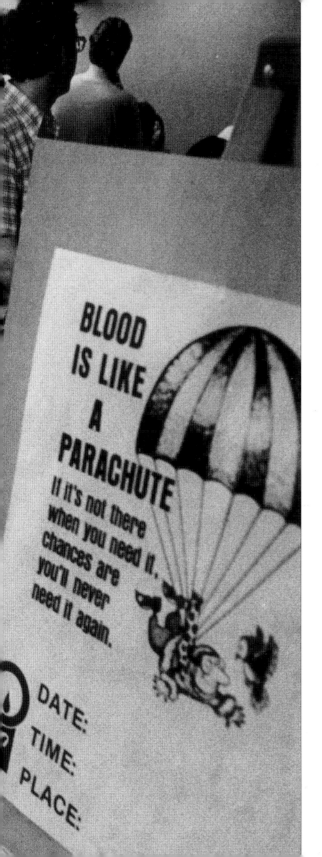

The Hyatt disaster exposed communications shortcomings. The media, for instance, was told to spread the word that blood donors were needed, but that information did not go to the nearby Community Blood Center. Residents eager to help injured victims descended upon the blood bank, which was not ready to handle that many people.

Potential donors lined up at the Community Blood Center at 4040 Main St. eager to donate blood after a plea for volunteers was issued.

William H. Batson, The Times

> "Every response and every incident is not the same. We had a plan, but we didn't have a plan for this type of incident."

Arnett Williams, deputy fire chief and incident commander on July 17, 1981

The city had created a plan called Operation Bulldozer, implemented after the 1957 Ruskin Heights area tornado that killed 35 people. It was a pre-arrangement for construction companies to supply bulldozers, forklifts and other equipment and personnel to disasters.

But bulldozers were of no use at the Hyatt and the first forklifts were too small to lift the skywalks. Operation Bulldozer was expanded after the skywalks disaster to have larger equipment, such as cranes, available as well.

Arnett Williams, a deputy fire chief who became incident commander at the scene, said a lesson from the Hyatt is to have enough resources — no matter how large or small the disaster scene. Catastrophe can result from something as comparatively simple as a car accident where rescue workers lack necessary equipment to help a dying victim, he said.

"If you deplete your resources, even if it is one piece of equipment, that is a catastrophe," Williams said. That is the message Williams took to emergency preparedness training seminars after the Hyatt incident.

"Every response and every incident is not the same," Williams said. "We had a plan, but we didn't have a plan for this type of incident."

Today, the response to an event similar to the disaster of July 1981 would be more effective, Dyer said. For starters, the fire department is much better trained and equipped than it was years ago.

"Thirty years ago we were still built around the idea that the fire department was in the business to fight fires," Dyer said. "We had few other collateral jobs. Today, it's a multi-faceted emergency response organization."

Department personnel are trained from the bottom up, not just in fighting fires but in emergency medical care, hazardous materials responses and a wide range of technical rescues, Dyer said.

If the skywalks had collapsed today, they would have been disassembled and removed much more quickly, Dyer said.

Special concrete saws, not jackhammers, would grind away the concrete surface to reach victims. Air bags, not cranes, would be used

GARY FRANK

"It was as if we were a honeycomb in a beehive. People were swarming the ambulances looking for help."

Emergency Medical Technician Gary Frank wasn't supposed to work the night of the Hyatt disaster, but he reluctantly agreed to work the shift of an employee who wanted the night off.

Friday nights could be busy, but that description would fall far short of what awaited the 22-year-old EMT.

The dispatcher said there was a roof collapse at the hotel. That was hard to understand because the building was new, Frank thought, as he and paramedic Gary Trinidad sped to the scene from their post at 27th Street and Holmes. At 7:11 p.m., their ambulance would be the first to arrive outside the hotel, Frank said.

Trinidad raced inside. As Frank stepped outside the ambulance, dazed and bleeding people started approaching him.

"First, a gentleman walked up to me and said, 'Sir, can you help me, I have a headache,'" Frank said. "His ear was missing. Right behind him was a lady. I saw her bleeding on the inside of her arm. She said, 'I am a free bleeder.' I gave them both gauze and asked them to roll each other's wounds shut."

More people came up to Frank for help: One had chest pains, another bones sticking out of his skin, yet another with half his head scraped and bleeding. Some people had blank stares on their faces. Frank could not understand what could have happened inside the building.

Within minutes, other ambulances had arrived and their EMTs immediately leapt into action.

"It was as if we were a honeycomb in a beehive," Frank said. "People were swarming the ambulances looking for help."

Frank did not get inside the building for two or three hours because there was so much to do outside.

A "conveyor belt of ambulances" was established to transport people, mostly to one of four hospitals that were within three minutes of the hotel, Frank said.

Frank was on duty until 8:30 or 9 the next morning, he said. He went home, wrapped his blood-encrusted clothes and shoes in a trash bag and tossed them in the closet, where they stayed for a week. He could not sleep that first day or night after he got home.

Frank decided to write down all that he experienced. He felt a need to spill it all out. His report was published in the Journal of Emergency Medical Services. In it he wrote about not knowing what had happened until he went inside the hotel.

"I walked in to see what monster had inflicted this on people," Frank wrote. "I could smell death. I saw a head and arm not connected to a torso. I saw a priest giving last rites standing in a pool of blood."

Frank knew he had gone through an experience that would stick with him all of his life. But in retrospect he was glad he was there to help people on that grimmest of nights. The title of his report: "Never Regret Working for a Friend."

Mayor Richard Berkley wiped away a tear during a special meeting of the City Council after he announced the death of John Tvedten Sr., an off-duty fire battalion chief who died in the collapse of the skywalks.

Thousands were at risk

One week after the disaster, a public meeting and forum was held to address any mental health issues or psychological trauma that anyone might be experiencing as a result of the tragedy. People were invited to speak out, to share their experiences and to learn about help that was available.

According to a fact sheet handed out at the meeting, almost 5,000 Kansas Citians were close enough to the disaster to have been placed at psychological risk.

THEY INCLUDED:

– Almost 200 injured.
– Estimated 456 relatives of those who died.
– Estimated 732 relatives of those who were injured.
– 1,500 uninjured bystanders.
– 1,000 rescue workers.
– 500 hotel workers.
– 250 medical personnel.
– 150 members of the media.

Source: Kansas City Star/Times July 25, 1981

John Spink, The Times

Deputy fire chief Arnett Williams addressed a crowd that had gathered at Pierson Hall on the campus of UMKC to listen to advice from mental health experts and to discuss how they were handing the aftermath. Many cited depression, apathy, irritability, inability to sleep and memory lapses.

to lift the heavy skywalk beams. Inflated by compressors, these air bags have been used at accident scenes to lift semi-tractor trailers and can lift much more than that, Dyer said.

Dyer said he has no doubt that today's planning, training and equipment would have saved more lives at the Hyatt disaster scene, where some people bled to death waiting to be rescued and treated.

"We'd be much faster than we were 30 years ago," Dyer said.

At the scene, a fire and police commander would be assigned immediately to take charge of organizing the rescue. They would assess

Red Cross worker Billie Miller received a comforting embrace from a colleague and fellow mourner during a memorial Mass at Immaculate Conception Cathedral. Miller was a veteran disaster field representative who had arrived at the Hyatt about 15 minutes after the collapse of the skywalks.

EDITORIAL FROM
THE KANSAS CITY TIMES,
July 20, 1981

Kansas City is left numb by a flood of grief and shock that only can be expressed in one word of agonized bewilderment: "Why?"

Anger will come later. For now, an aching sorrow pierces the heart of the city. People who had gone to a place of fun to find a few moments of their youth found death. Families of loving men and women and children were demolished. The sound of music turned into a crackling noise of horror, then became a boom and then a crash, and then an uncomprehending silence for one suspended moment of time.

But whatever investigations over the months ahead disclose, we can imagine no easy answer to that question, "Why?" New hotel structures are not supposed to collapse. The roofs of vast arenas, such as the Kemper, are not supposed to fall. New hotels in Las Vegas or anywhere else are not supposed to fill with flames and poisonous smoke. Bridges not many years old are not supposed to wear out.

It is impossible not to ask whether the people who are relied upon to design and put up safe, accommodating structures know what they are doing, and whether the people who are supposed to inspect and test them know much more.

The basic purpose of any structure is to provide shelter — a word meaning refuge, an area of safety, a defense against injury, exposure, attack. When the shelter attacks the innocents within, then the very reason for the existence of shelter is turned upside down. The section of society that created the thing is not working. The man-made maze of design, construction, inspection and use, all the elaborate institutions that caused it to be built, have failed. Something is deeply wrong.

The Kemper roof collapsed two years ago on an empty floor. The wildly improbable good luck that attended that potential disaster must have made us think that such things can't happen here. So Kansas City waited for its Hyatt Regency dance of death.

WHY?

Lee Judge, The Times

JOE WAECKERLE

Emergency room physician Joe Waeckerle had wrapped up his shift at Baptist Medical Center in Kansas City in the early evening. He topped off his workday by running up and down 11 flights of stairs at the hospital to help him get ready for the rugby season.

When he stopped off at ER, the phone rang from dispatchers asking him to report to the Hyatt. A call had gone out to all area hospitals about possible mass casualties from some sort of accident at the hotel. Waeckerle, in his blue surgical scrubs, jumped in his car.

Waeckerle arrived at the hotel about 12 minutes after the collapse and was checking victims outside when he was quickly told that the most seriously hurt people were inside.

He rushed inside the building and was immediately overwhelmed by what he saw: people dead and alive protruding from the collapsed skywalks or tangled in other debris.

"It took my breath away for 15 or 30 seconds," Waeckerle said. "I didn't know where to start, but it was time to get to work and do what I was trained to do."

Waeckerle, 35 at the time, had been the recent director of the emergency medical system in Kansas City so he became medical officer in charge of rescue and triage at the scene.

Other doctors were there to help, along with caregivers who could tend to or at least talk to trapped victims while they waited for rescue workers. Waeckerle had to categorize the victims to determine how and in what order they could be attended to medically.

"There were people who were trapped who were not going to survive no matter what I did," he said. "Some were going to live no matter what I did and there were those in between."

Emotional support was given to victims who had no chance to survive, he said, including one woman who was pinned hopelessly under the skywalk but had not bled out because major vessels were pinched shut by pressure from the weight on top of her.

"Her friends and family asked that I do something," he said. "They were begging in plaintive cries, but there was nothing I could do for her. I have particular nightmares about that one."

Another harrowing incident involved a man whose only slim chance of being saved was to have his leg amputated so he could be freed of the wreckage. Waeckerle explained to the man his grim choice: lose a leg or die for sure.

Firefighters and others tried to comfort the victim, Jeff Durham, a real estate agent and part-time bartender in Westport. Waeckerle administered morphine, and another physician cut the leg off with a chain saw. But Durham was too severely injured and died.

For all the people Waeckerle and other doctors and medics could not save, there were others who lived because of the emergency care they received. In all, 188 injured people survived the disaster, includ-

*"It took my breath away for
15 or 30 seconds.
I didn't know where to start,
but it was time to get to work and
do what I was trained to do."*

ing 22 trapped between the upper and lower skywalks and seven at the bottom of the stack, the fire department reported.

Waeckerle earned widespread praise for his work that night, but he said credit has to be shared by all of the doctors, EMTs, nurses and other professionals.

Some people could not deal with the graveness of treating trapped people and were assigned to other patients at the scene or to hospital emergency rooms, Waeckerle said. Others were capable of "divorcing themselves from reality" and giving care on the scene to patients in the most desperate of circumstances, he said.

"Everyone was in some way extraordinary in what they did," Waeckerle said. "But they were challenged."

Life and death decisions

With one of the hanger rods jutting diagonally into the air, rescue workers cleared wreckage and assist the injured. Joe Waeckerle, in surgical scrubs and wearing a stethoscope, is facing the cluster of men at lower right. He took charge of the immediate medical response inside the lobby and had to make decisions based on victims' chances of survival.

John Spink, The Times

Grief counseling

"This tragedy here in Kansas City has aroused the world. My heart goes out to the families of those who died and to those who were injured." Those were the words of the Rev. Billy Graham after meeting with injured patients at Truman Medical Center. Graham was in town just after the disaster, taking part in the American Festival of Evangelism.

Facing page: Graham met with Sandy Berkley, wife of Mayor Richard Berkley, before visiting injured victims Mark Williams, Tom Weir, Ed Bailey, Evelyn Gubar, Charles Wise and E.O. Gerster at Truman Medical Center.

Right: Mayor Richard Berkley paused at a wreath commemorating those who had died. At the time, the number of deaths stood at 111. Three more would die from the injuries they had suffered.

Cliff Schiappa, The Times

THEY WERE THERE

"Being there on both those days and having survived does make you pause. It has given me perspective on what is truly valuable in life."

ELLISON WALCOTT

Ellison Walcott struggled for 20 years to cope emotionally with what she had witnessed the night the skywalks collapsed at the Hyatt, where she worked.

Then, on Sept. 11, 2001, came another shock when she was outside the World Trade Center in the midst of the terrorist attacks.

"It has affected my whole life," Walcott said. "I don't think I've gotten over the trauma of witnessing both events."

Walcott worked as a valet, parking cars at the Hyatt the night of July 17, 1981. She was retrieving vehicles with another valet in the garage under the lobby when they heard a loud crash. Concrete pieces the size of small rocks shook out from the ceiling.

"I thought something was going to fall through and land on top of us," Walcott said. "We both rushed upstairs to the front of the Hyatt. I heard people screaming, and there were lots of people rushing around."

Walcott went inside and helped bandage victims. "People's eyes were glazed over, like sleepwalkers," Walcott recalled. "It seemed like the trail of injured would never end."

After about five hours, one of her bosses told her it would be a good idea to go home. She was reluctant but also exhausted and dispirited from the suffering she'd witnessed.

Walcott moved to New York in 1997. In September 2001, she worked as a temp in an office building adjacent to the World Trade Center.

She had just gotten off the subway when she witnessed the second of two terrorist-piloted jetliners hit the trade towers.

For the second time in her life, Walcott was among frantic and frightened crowds of people who had witnessed a horrifying calamity.

Walcott later moved back to Kansas City but returned to New York to live in 2010.

Not many people have borne witness to two disasters the scale of the Hyatt and World Trade Center.

"Being there on both those days and having survived does make you pause," Walcott says. "Some people believe that surviving tragic events means they have some greater purpose. I don't believe that. I am no greater and definitely not as brave as a soldier or as a war zone survivor. I am just lucky. It has given me perspective on what is truly valuable in life."

"We came in with a band aid for a wound that needed a tourniquet."

Richard Gist, psychologist and consultant for the Kansas City Fire Department.

Gist, who helped provide counseling for those traumatized by the catastrophe, says today's emergency personnel are in a better position to deal emotionally with catastrophic events.

the situation, assign responsibilities and determine what should be accomplished in the first minutes, first hour, second hour, etc., Dyer said.

Hospitals would be notified of the potential for mass casualties. That was the case 30 years ago at the Hyatt, but today information would flow in both directions. Each trauma center would respond as to how many patients they can accommodate, based on available rooms, surgery suites, staff and other factors.

Kansas City isn't the only community in the metro area to have a comprehensive plan for responding to accidents, terrorism or other disasters large and small, Dyer said.

Under a regional rescue system set up through the Mid-America Regional Council and funded with federal Homeland Security grants, six units in the metro area have comparable expertise. Three of the units are part of the KCFD and one each is in Kansas City, Kan., Olathe, and the Central Jackson County Fire Department in Blue Springs.

Superior training and better equipment also can help in ways not immediately apparent.

Some firefighters, police and other emergency responders struggled mightily in the wake of the Hyatt, partly because they felt unable to do more for dying victims. Richard Gist, a psychologist who studied the disaster and is a consultant to the KCFD, said today's emergency personnel are in a better position to deal emotionally with catastrophic events.

"It makes all the difference in the world if you come away from something knowing you did what you could do, you did what you had to do, and the outcome was out of your control," Gist said. "You knew the plan was rehearsed and it was organized."

Two days after the skywalks disaster, rescue workers, survivors, relatives of the dead and others who felt traumatized by the event were invited to meet with counselors at the Swope Parkway Mental Health Center, Gist said. But that approach proved too general, too soon and too shallow, Gist said.

"We came in with a band aid for a wound that needed a tourniquet," Gist said.

The support that people needed was more complex and individual than calling everyone into what amounted to a group therapy session, he said. Not everyone had the same experience or the same reaction to what they saw. Some didn't want or need to talk about it with counselors or each other — that day or maybe ever.

Counselors tried a different tactic a week later. Knowing there was saturation media coverage of the disaster, they publicized a variety of ways people could get help dealing with their feelings. They could meet with counselors or with other witnesses and survivors.

"We wanted to give them some time to settle in and understand what they were looking for," Gist said.

People came forward in their own time and on their own terms for help, Gist said. Subsequent study found a wide range of how much and what kind of counseling people needed. Some didn't seek any help at all.

Despite the effectiveness of giving traumatized people time and space, there was in later years a rush to help people who survived catastrophes. Immediately after the 9/11 terrorist attacks, for instance, thousands of counselors and crisis intervention specialists descended on New York to offer an ear to grieving and traumatized rescue workers and survivors.

That triggered a backlash to what amounted to intervention overkill. In the years since 9/11 the school-of-thought pendulum has swung back to what Gist and other counselors learned in Kansas City: Less can sometimes be more.

"It was a very novel thing we did after the Hyatt," Gist said. "So the tendency is to think that if a little bit of it was good, a lot of it must be really good."

Victims and witnesses must certainly be made aware what kind of help is available, but not have it foisted upon them, Gist said. That became one of the lessons from the skywalks disaster that withstood the test of time.

CHAPTER 5

LIVES CHANGED FOREVER

Some have spent 30 years trying to cope with the grim images of that night.

By Kevin Murphy

Thirty years is a long time to live in the shadow of a tragedy. Those who survived the collapse of the Hyatt skywalks or who treated victims or lost a loved one have managed in their own ways to move on from that night.

But for many, it has not been easy.

Some escaped death, only to live a life of physical or emotional pain that challenged their spirit and altered the course of their lives.

Some who were heroes wished deeply that they never had the chance to be one.

Others chose not to talk about the event for years or to this day flinch at loud noises or glance warily upward when entering some buildings.

In fact, a whole community has not been quite the same since that summer night in 1981.

"It's taken a toll," said Charley Fisher, former Kansas City fire chief who was deputy chief on the night of the Hyatt disaster. "Thousands of peoples' lives were changed forever."

Every one of those people has a different story to tell about that night and the long aftermath.

Ed Bailey is a Hyatt survivor whose brush with death forever taught him how life is fleeting. Bailey and his date, Shelley McQueeny, were watching the dancers that night when the skywalks came smashing down on top of them.

Had they been standing a foot away they might have been killed instantly. Bailey has always felt he got a lease on life that night. Ever since, he has not taken it for granted.

"You are here one minute and gone the next," Bailey said. "You are not promised tomorrow."

Bailey and McQueeny were among only a few people pulled alive from under the bottom skywalk. Their injuries were serious. He had two crushed ankles, a fractured hip and ruptured discs. She suffered back, pelvis and leg fractures.

In casts and bandages, Bailey and McQueeny recovered together at the hospital and later at her home for many long months. They bonded, drew closer and married. But it turned out their shared experience wasn't enough to make a strong marriage. They divorced after about two years.

Bailey practiced law in Kansas City and Independence for years

Aaron Leimkuehler, The Star

Shelley McQueeny

Aaron Leimkuehler, The Star

"People have problems, things happen. Maybe it's not fair that these things happened to me. But that's the way life is. I'm not bitter."

before retiring to Hot Springs, Ark., and then to southern Texas. Mc-Queeny, who already suffered from a serious lung disease at the time of the skywalks collapse, was a health care worker before her injuries. She stayed in Kansas City but never returned to work.

For the first five years, Bailey couldn't walk without the aid of crutches or a cane. He still suffers pain in his shoulder. McQueeny said she is in constant pain.

Bailey said he was puzzled and angry that he and others suffered because the design flaw was not detected.

"When you walk into a new building, you don't expect it to fall on your head," Bailey said.

McQueeny resents what she believes was the rush to complete construction of the Hyatt in the interest of money over safety. But she said she has never felt sorry for herself.

"People have problems, things happen," McQueeny said. "Maybe it's not fair that these things happened to me. But that's the way life is. I'm not bitter."

Bailey said he has never dwelled on that night but hasn't hidden his feelings, either.

"I've always been able to talk about it," he said.

Some people, however, dealt with emotional scars of that evening by not talking about it at all. For years — even with others who were there that night.

John and Marie Driscoll of Lee's Summit were at the Hyatt with three other couples. None of them was injured, but they witnessed the skywalks fall to the floor, crushing dozens of innocent people.

Over the years, the couples would socialize frequently, but John Driscoll said the topic of the Hyatt never came up in conversation. Maybe it was just too painful.

"I could not talk about it myself for a long time," said Driscoll, retired from General Motors. "Sometimes I would think about it at work, and tears would come to my eyes. I thought about all those people, dressed up, happy and having a good time. It's something I will never forget, and it's like it was yesterday."

Mike Falder, who was one of the first firefighters on the scene that night, gave lectures around the country for several years about the response to the collapse and lessons learned. But eventually revisiting such a painful night wasn't worth it emotionally.

"Between lectures, I put everything away, and then I'd have to take it out, talk about it and show the slides," Falder said.

About 20 years ago, he finally told Fire Chief Charley Fisher, "I'm not going to do it anymore." The experience also diminished his interest in seeking a promotion to battalion chief, he said.

Falder, now retired, didn't want to talk about that night for this book. He had relived it enough.

"I put it away years ago," Falder said.

■■■

Firefighters, police, emergency medical workers, construction crews and others who helped rescue victims that night were widely commended — none more so, perhaps, than Joseph Waeckerle.

An emergency medical doctor, Waeckerle worked all night at the Hyatt and supervised the triage. Waeckerle treated and consoled patients and made tough choices on who should be treated and who was beyond help.

Waeckerle got a lot of recognition, appeared in national news magazines and on programs such as the "The Today Show."

But while finding himself portrayed as a hero, Waeckerle wished he never had been put into that position.

"That was probably harder for me to deal with than the event itself," Waeckerle said. "All those people had to die for me to be recognized."

In the months that followed the disaster he frequently got calls from rescue workers, including a man who operated a jackhammer to reach trapped victims. They just wanted to talk through their feelings with him, Waeckerle said.

"It was a brotherhood of people who shared an experience," he said. "A bonding occurs when you go through this."

Waeckerle in recent years has practiced sports injury medicine, specializing in concussions and other brain trauma. He is a consultant for the NFL and the NFL Players Association, as well as high school

Marie and John Driscoll

Aaron Leimkuehler, The Star

"I thought about all those people, dressed up, happy and having a good time. It's something I will never forget."

John Driscoll

Anyone who was in the lobby of the Hyatt Regency hotel at the time of the disaster qualified for a $1,000 cash settlement. Lawyers for Hallmark Cards and Crown Center Redevelopment Corp. filled out application forms of those who had claims. In one morning, more than 150 people filed claims, and by noon $112,000 had been disbursed.

PAYING THE PRICE

The collapse of the Hyatt skywalks immediately triggered scores of lawsuits by victims and relatives. Total claims sought in state and federal court would exceed $3.5 billion within four months, according to Hallmark Cards Inc. officials.

Hallmark and its wholly owned subsidiary at the time, Crown Center Redevelopment Corp., were defendants along with the Hyatt corporation, project architects, managers and contractors, the city of Kansas City and others.

The cause of the collapse was traced to faulty design of support rods that suspended the two skywalks from the ceiling.

Among defendants in the lawsuits, only the Hyatt and Hallmark had the "deep pockets" to pay large settlements, Donald J. Hall, Hallmark president at the time, stated in the company's 100th anniversary book in 2009. But $3.5 billion would have put Hallmark out of business, Hall said, so lawyers for the company and other defendants negotiated a plan for settlements.

Hallmark decided to admit liability in the case and to guarantee settlements, though insurance ended up covering the payments, corporate officials said. In all, about 1,600 claimants received roughly $140 million, mostly from Hallmark and Hyatt insurers.

The individual amounts reached millions of dollars for some plaintiffs, but everyone who was at the tea dance that night was eligible to receive $1,000, whether injured or not. Only a handful of cases went to trial to determine judgment amounts, and the rest of the cases were settled out of court.

— *Kevin Murphy*

---

athletic programs.

The Hyatt experience still resurrects anger, he said.

"It was an unnecessary tragedy had people done their jobs," Waeckerle said.

■ ■ ■

Sally Firestone feels the same way.

Firestone was the most seriously injured of the Hyatt survivors. She had gone to the tea dance with three friends and was on the second-level skywalk when it collapsed. Firestone lay unconscious and didn't come to until she was in the hospital two hours after the collapse.

After three months in ICU and four months at a rehabilitation hospital, she returned to her second-floor walk-up apartment. Wheelchair-accessible housing was scarce in 1982. An adaptable apartment space was found, and she returned to her job for a few years.

Firestone, 64, has spent her life since the accident using a wheelchair as a quadriplegic. She requires assistance and lives in a senior living community in south Kansas City. She doesn't harbor bitterness, but is disappointed that flaws in the skywalk design got past engineers and other professionals.

"There were a number of checks along the way where it should have been caught," Firestone said. "I wish building inspectors would have done their jobs properly."

Firestone said she has made the best of her life with the help of family and friends. She has been active on boards and committees of non-profit organizations such as Kansas City Academy and Saint Paul School of Theology, as well as her church, Central United Methodist.

Firestone has also served on the advisory committee for the Rehabilitation Institute of Kansas City and reStart Inc., an interfaith ministry that provides shelter and services for the homeless.

■ ■ ■

For Frank Freeman, pain is a perpetual reminder of that night at the Hyatt.

The Kansas City businessman suffered injuries to discs in his neck and lower back when the falling skywalks grazed him and killed his partner, Roger Grigsby.

Freeman suffered for years before finally getting surgery in 2005, when doctors put two metal plates, six metal pins and four cadaver bones along vertebrae in his neck. The surgery came on the heels of a heart attack in 2004, he said. Discs in his neck and spine still need repair.

Beside surgery, he used neck stretchers, electrode treatments and so many different kinds of medication that he finally quit because they disoriented him to the point where "I didn't know if I was coming or going."

Freeman said pain is the price he pays for giving up medication.

"When the pain increased, I just told myself I'm going to have to live with it."

He also struggled for years with guilt about so narrowly escaping death when Grigsby and so many others died.

"Why me?" he would ask himself. "I felt like I didn't deserve to be here."

Freeman said the passing years gradually erased his guilt, but not his anger. He remains upset, and not just about the design flaws that caused the collapse. He is still angry that a court order was required for investigators to examine the skywalk pieces, which were stored in a warehouse after the collapse.

Hallmark Inc. owned the building. The day after the collapse, Hallmark President Donald J. Hall issued a statement calling the prior 18 hours "the darkest of my life" and expressing his compassion and grief over what happened.

But Freeman has wanted something more from Hallmark officials all these years.

"I never heard an apology," he said. "Neither Hallmark nor the Hyatt ever issued any kind of statement in that regard."

Freeman said he would not buy a Hallmark card and returned any he received to the sender, a position he held for 28 years until 2009, when Hallmark donated $25,000 to a fund to build a memorial to victims and rescue crews.

Hallmark, too, has suffered from the tragedy, said Steve Doyal, senior vice president for public affairs and communication, in a state-ment for this book.

"The skywalks collapse was a tragedy for everyone involved and all of Kansas City," Doyal said. "For Hallmark and our employees, two of whom were killed, the loss was shattering, as was the realization of its devastating impact on the lives of so many in our city."

In a 2009 book commemorating Hallmark's 100th anniversary, Hall and former Hallmark general counsel Charles Egan reflected on the Hyatt disaster and the legal aftermath. Hall said that battles with insurance companies and emotional negotiations with victims weighed heavily upon him.

"I was tired," he is quoted in the Hallmark book. "It was demolishing."

While the cause of the collapse was traced to the design flaws, Hallmark agreed to admit liability and to fund settlements reported at more than $140 million.

"We have deep empathy for those whose lives were forever changed that night in 1981," Doyal said, "and hope that Hallmark's actions to address their needs as quickly as possible in the days and months that followed reflect our concern for what they experienced."

Freeman said Doyal's recent statements were important in demonstrating the Hall family's sense of grief and empathy.

"That is the best statement I have heard out of the Halls," Freeman said. "At least they acknowledged those killed and the devastating impact on the lives of so many in our city."

■ ■ ■

Of all the survivors of the Hyatt collapse, Mark Williams had perhaps the most harrowing experience.

Williams, 34 at the time, was trapped under the bottom skywalk, his legs spread in the splits and pulled out of their hip sockets. First he was nearly crushed to death. Then, water from a broken pipe edged up just beneath his mouth before receding. Finally, rescuers nearly pierced him with a jackhammer.

Williams was the last person pulled alive from under the skywalks — some nine and a half hours after the collapse.

He said he always thought he would live through the experience.

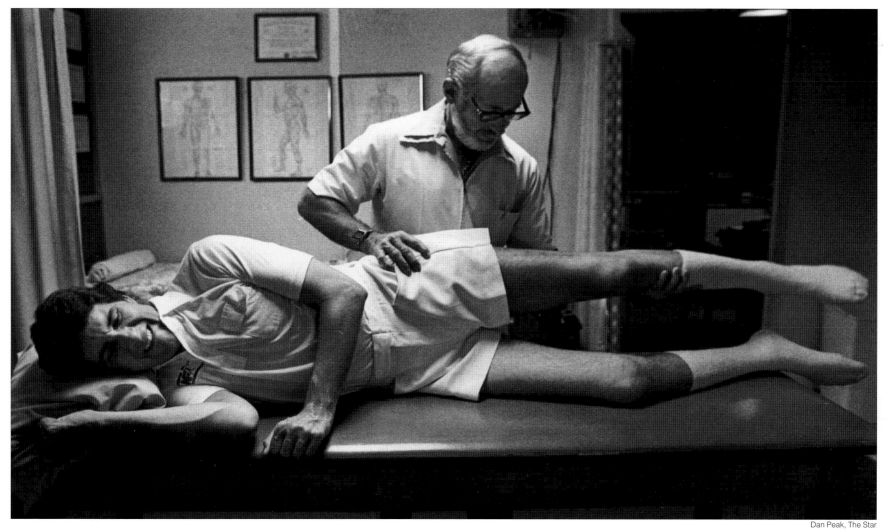

Physical therapist Bill Dunn helped Mark Williams with exercises to strengthen his fractured body. Williams suffered catastrophic injuries to his legs and hips and faced months of therapy.

MARK WILLIAMS

Mark Williams, a real estate appraiser, was standing in line for a drink at the bar when he heard what sounded like snapping metal. He sensed something falling and knew he had to get as close to the ground as possible.

Williams, a fit 34-year-old, dropped immediately into the splits. When the piggybacked skywalks came to a crashing halt, Williams became trapped underneath in a dark space less than 18 inches high. Both his legs tore loose from their hip sockets. His left ankle was pressed against his right ear. His back was twisted, his nose broken, his scalp lacerated.

But Williams' biggest concern was drowning from water that was spilling onto the floor from a broken pipe high above the lobby. It edged closer and closer to his nose and mouth before the water was shut off and began receding.

Williams could hear the voice of an 11-year-old girl, Pamela Coffey, trapped near him. She was severely hurt and her father had been crushed to death, though she didn't know it, Williams said. Coffey kept saying the Lord's Prayer, Williams said, but soon the little girl's voice trailed off and she died.

Williams was trapped for hours in cramped, hot and humid darkness. Then, he heard the sounds of a jackhammer pounding away on the concrete deck above him. Rescue workers were trying to cut through to string a crane cable through and could not hear Williams yelling for help.

The tip of the jackhammer brushed the edges of his arm, ribs and legs. He had survived the collapse, had nearly drowned, and now he was in danger of being pierced by a jackhammer.

Finally, there was a pause in the hammering and Williams yelled out. "You idiots! Shut off that jackhammer." He heard someone say, "There is someone alive in there."

A large forklift edged under the skywalk and lifted it up to free

Todd Feeback, The Star

Williams nine and a half hours after the collapse. Williams felt a rush of cool air. He sat up at last, though his body was twisted and broken. Later that night, miraculously, he found his sense of humor. Holding up his Timex wristwatch, he told rescuers, "It's still ticking."

Williams was the last person rescued from the disaster. He was told by several people later that he was the only one of about 25 people in line for a drink who did not get killed.

"I never did think I was going to die," Williams said. "I don't think that way."

He kept the same sturdy outlook over the past 30 years, despite his injuries, which left him without use of his left foot and only partial use of his right foot.

"It changed me for the better," Williams said. "I found out more of what I was made of and maybe became not so self-centered. They say what doesn't kill you makes you stronger. Most people are never tested, so they never find out what they can be."

■ ■ ■

Few people could find humor in injuries they suffered in the skywalk, but Sol Koenigsberg has managed to do so.

After suffering a broken back and leg in the skywalks collapse, Koenigsberg said the most lasting physical effect 30 years later is knowing when rainy weather is on the way because his back acts up.

"I'm a good long-range weather forecaster," he says. "I can tell 24 to 48 hours in advance if the pressure is dropping."

When a storm arrives, it is his wife, Rosette, who suffers. She received only minor injuries in the collapse, but thunderstorms cause her to scream, he said. She is also startled by other unexpected sounds. Sol tries to be quiet around the house.

"After 30 years, she can't bear sudden noises, especially ones she can't identify," he said.

■ ■ ■

Barbara Younger can associate with that. Younger, who was at the Hyatt that night, said the skywalks collapse sounded like the crack of tree limbs in a storm.

"For a long time, the sound of thunder or anything like that freaked me out," Younger said.

■ ■ ■

For Cheryl Taylor, the problem isn't so much the sounds as it is the presence of ceilings. Taylor was standing near the front door of the Hyatt, and she narrowly missed getting hit by the falling skywalks.

"I never did think I was going to die. I don't think that way."

Mark Williams, the last person pulled alive from under the skywalks, more than nine hours after the collapse

133

FOR THE LOVE
OF HIS MOTHER

John Sullivan lost his mother, Kathryn "Katy" Sullivan, in the disaster. Her death shattered the lives of the Sullivan family. John became an attorney, moved to Texas and started a new life there, far from the reminders of the disaster. When his daughter was born on the birthday of his mother, March 21, he and his wife named the baby Kathryn.

Kathryn "Katy" Sullivan

John Sullivan

BETTY NELSON

"I can still hear her say it ... 'Oh, kid.'
Just once I'd love to hear her say that again."

Betty Nelson and her husband, Fred, went to the Hyatt in the afternoon and ran into close friends Katy and Bob Sullivan. They thought the dance would be fun. Big band music, dancing, a nice evening out.

While their husbands retreated to an alcove with the crowd, Betty and Katy wanted to get closer to the dance floor to watch the band and dancers. They were standing only about a foot apart. Suddenly, over the sound of the band's rendition of "Satin Doll," Nelson heard something.

"It sounded like the wind, a rush of air," Nelson said. "Out of the corner of my eye, I saw something move toward us. I couldn't figure out what it was. By the time I could react, it was too late."

The skywalks landed on top of the two women, crushing Sullivan to death but sparing Nelson. She thinks she was saved by the underside design of the skywalk, which had cavities every few feet between its supports. But she was pinned to the tile floor by the structure, barely able to move.

Nelson suffered a broken left leg and ankle, cracked ribs and other injuries. But as water from the broken pipe started to rise, she remembers, she was mostly concerned about keeping her new high heel shoes and her diamond wristwatch — a birthday present from her husband — dry.

"It's crazy the things you think about," Nelson said.

Nelson was lying on the floor in near darkness with another woman on top of her.

"I can still see her blouse — yellow. And it had pink flowers on it," Nelson said. "I talked to her, but she never talked to me. She was groaning. She died lying on top of me. I never found out her name."

A man's foot was pinned by Nelson's side. He wore brown shoes and socks, and his foot was straight up, but then it went limp, she recalled.

Nelson called out for Katy but never got a response.

"There was so much noise and people moaning and groaning," Nelson said. "I kept thinking, 'Why can't they lift this thing up?' I didn't know it was a skywalk."

After three hours, firemen and other rescue workers had raised the skywalk slightly to reach victims. A fireman crawled in on his belly, dragged out the dead man who was next to Nelson. But he could not get her out until he pulled the dead woman off of her. Finally, he dragged Nelson by her armpits away from the wreckage. Her husband came running up to her. Sullivan asked about Katy, but Nelson didn't have an answer.

In the hospital at 3 a.m., the Sullivans' son John called Nelson to ask about his mother, but she still wasn't sure what had happened. Later that morning, Fred Nelson told his wife that Katy had died.

Reminders of the collapse turned up hours later when Fred Nelson pulled a handkerchief from his jacket, dislodging several bits of glass.

"It was a horrible, terrible tragedy, but I was so blessed the Lord saw fit to see that I was OK," Nelson said. She and Katy Sullivan had been friends through their kids' school years, Little League, PTA meetings and other activities.

Katy Sullivan was always known to use the phrase "oh, kid."

"I can still hear her say it ... 'Oh, kid,' " Nelson said. "Just once I'd love to hear her say that again."

A woman she was talking with was crushed to death while Taylor suffered only scrapes.

"I could not go back into the Hyatt for many years," Taylor said. "I am still very fearful of any kind of building where there is an overhang. I look up to make sure there is nothing dangerous that could fall."

■ ■ ■

Among victims of the Hyatt tragedy are relatives of those who died. Thousands of people lost mothers, fathers, siblings, children and other loved ones in the skywalks collapse.

Brent Wright lost his mother, Karen Jeter, and his stepfather, Eugene Jeter, in the skywalks disaster. The couple had married 16 days earlier in Loose Park. They were happy and one of the things they liked to do was dance, said Wright, who was 17 in July 1981.

The couple is seen smiling and dancing in a television video just minutes before the skywalks collapsed. KMBC-TV was filming a feature on the tea dance. The footage was widely shown, including on ABC's "20/20" three days after the disaster.

"That was painful to watch at the beginning, but as time goes by we filter out the bad memories and keep the good memories," Wright said. "We know they were doing what they loved to do."

Wright became an attorney and practices law in a high-rise building across from the Hyatt. " I see it out my office window every day," Wright said.

Just as with the video, Wright has not let the everyday presence of the Hyatt take him back to that dark day.

"With time, I tend to focus on the positive things," Wright said. "We need to live our lives and be happy, productive people. So I chose not to let what happened define me or my life."

■ ■ ■

John Sullivan, who lost his mother, Kathryn "Katy" Sullivan, in the skywalk collapse, also moved on with his life after the disaster and he, too, became a lawyer.

But unlike Wright, Sullivan was uncomfortable with the 40-story profile of the Hyatt in the skyline south of downtown Kansas City. He decided as a young lawyer to move to the Dallas area to practice. In Kansas City, he knew he would have worked somewhere downtown not far from the Hyatt.

"You can't miss the thing, it's a daily reminder," Sullivan said. "I'm not saying it was an overriding thing, I'm not sure it was a conscious thing." But Sullivan moved away nonetheless.

Sullivan said his mother's death was very hard on his father, Bob Sullivan, who was with her that night. The couple ran a hardware store for many years in downtown Blue Springs, but had sold the business. They finally had time to enjoy life, Sullivan said.

Sullivan's mother was the more outgoing of the couple and he said it would be just like her to want to get up close to watch the dance contest. Bob Sullivan never remarried and he died in 2000.

Sullivan named his daughter Kathryn after his mother. She was born in 2004, on March 21, the same birthday as her grandmother.

■ ■ ■

Cathy Pitts of Wamego, Kan., has missed her mother for the past 30 years, but the heartbreak was especially strong a few years ago when she turned 53 — the age of her mom when she died at the Hyatt.

"It hit me hard," Pitts said. "It's not that old."

Laurette and Ray Glover of Merriam, Kan., her parents, had gone to prior tea dances and were there with another couple, Robert and Mary Torrey of Roeland Park, Kan., on the night of the collapse.

Pitts said she was deeply affected by the death of her parents, particularly the loss of her mother, who was a teacher at Milburn Junior High School. When Pitts was older and experiencing personal problems, she missed the important counsel and support from her parents.

"It definitely changed the direction of my life," she said.

Pitts said the tragedy also made her more of a worrier and protective of her son as he was growing up.

"So many people don't think things will happen to them," she said. "I knew that anything could happen. It changed the way I look at everything."

Aaron Leimkuehler, The Star

Eugene and Karen Jeter, Brent Wright's stepfather and mother, died doing what they loved.

"As time goes by, we filter out the bad memories and keep the good memories."

Brent Wright

He had a story to share

In the days following the collapse, as bereaved families huddled in grief and some of the wounded came to grips with grim diagnoses, the family of gravely injured John Dixon had a story to share.

It would console some. It would inspire others. It was the story of Dixon himself.

Dixon, 64, a paraplegic for the previous 26 years, had watched the tea dance at the Hyatt from his wheelchair on the second-story skywalk. He and his wife, Dorothy, survived the fall, but falling debris smashed his wheelchair and crushed his chest. At Veterans Hospital, doctors struggled to keep him alive. One leg was shattered, his face was busted up, and his pulverized skin, already paper-thin from decades in a wheelchair, put him at risk of a lethal infection. The doctors had told the family the outlook did not look good.

But Dixon was conscious and talking, and Dorothy and his children still felt the power of this charismatic leader, a man the U.S. Navy called a war hero. And at the hospital, as they read newspaper accounts of other families in similar situations, they knew that a few words from Jeff, as they called him, might go a long way, especially with those who were paralyzed or otherwise crippled in the skywalks collapse. So only a few days after the skywalks fell, as Dixon teetered between life and death in the intensive care unit, they invited editors at The Star to send a reporter to Veterans Hospital. They felt so strongly about this that when they learned that only close family members could enter the ICU, they deputized the reporter as a "beloved cousin."

"A family copes best with this if the patient is a man like my husband," Dorothy Lee Dixon said. "He's the strongest man I

John "Jeff" Dixon, a decorated Navy pilot and World War II veteran, was confined to a wheelchair for 26 years. Before he died, becoming the last of the 114 fatalities, he shared his uplifting story and offered hope to others who were injured in the catastrophe.

know."

She said her husband's upbeat outlook on life would inspire anyone, injured or healthy.

In the ICU, Dixon gave a firm handshake, his hands and face entwined with the green medical tubes sustaining his life. His crushed chest could barely push enough air to make words. He said the story should be about his heroic nurses, and not about him, but Dorothy reminded him about crippled Hyatt survivors. Dixon nodded, gathered himself. He had to stop in the middle of every sentence.

"They must accept their injuries and make the most of their lives. There are so many things you can do in a wheelchair. There are so many things you can't do — you can't walk, you can't dance … but you can still be a good person. You can still serve your fellow man."

He paused. His daughter Deborah offered him a bite of food, but he gently waved it off.

"Please mention those nurses' names. They've been so good to me."

Around him his children held his hands, touched him. They looked proud and upbeat.

In the Navy in World War II, Dixon was awarded the Distinguished Flying Cross, one of the nation's highest military awards for valor, for the anti-submarine and reconnaissance mission he'd flown. Ten years after the war, in a training exercise over the Olathe Naval Air Station, his fighter jet's engine had cut out at low altitude. Dixon stayed with the falling plane to steer it away from a cluster of houses. After it crashed, several men won medals of valor for pulling his broken and burned body out of the flames.

He spent a year in hospitals after that, and never once complained, Dorothy said.

Dixon, listening, shook his head. He said it embarrassed him

"God left me on Earth for some reason. What it was, I don't know – maybe it was to do the best I could with whatever I have."

to talk about himself.

He said that every bereaved family and every family struggling with injuries could look forward to a wonderful life once they got past grief and physical therapy. He said he had learned this himself, in his wheelchair.

"God left me on Earth for some reason. What it was, I don't know — maybe it was to do the best I could with whatever I have."

Dixon died on Dec. 1, 1981, four and a half months after the skywalks fell. Local authorities, seeing notice of his passing, raised the Hyatt death toll to 114; he was the last to die as a result of injuries suffered on July 17, 1981.

His children, who knew this was coming, had said at the hospital that their dad's last public act would be this interview, a gift of wisdom and compassion characteristic of a man who'd dispensed those virtues to others all his life.

— Roy Wenzl, former reporter for The Kansas City Star and "beloved cousin" of John "Jeff" Dixon

ONE FAMILY'S LOSS

"Quite honestly, it destroyed my life," Peggy Olson said, recounting the loss of her father, Gerald Coffey, and her 11-year-old sister, Pamela Coffey, the youngest victim of the skywalks collapse.

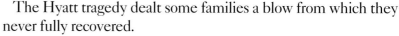

The Hyatt tragedy dealt some families a blow from which they never fully recovered.

"Quite honestly, it destroyed my life," said Peggy Olson, who was an adult when she lost her father, Gerald Coffey, and 11-year-old sister, Pamela Coffey, in the skywalks collapse. "It actually messed up our whole family."

Olson said that until a couple of years ago she could not even talk about their deaths without getting very emotional. Her mother still can't bear talking about it, Olson said.

Pamela Coffey was the youngest person killed at the Hyatt. Her parents were divorced, and that Friday night was her dad's turn to spend time with her. He decided to take her to the dance, but no one in the family knew until after reports of the skywalks collapse, Olson said.

"What I tell people all the time is that I think it's harder when you have someone die suddenly than if they were sick for a while," Olson said. "If they were sick, you at least had time to make amends, to talk about issues and resolve things."

Olson struggled not only with grief but anger, which built to a point that on the 25th anniversary of the collapse she wrote e-mails to architects and engineers responsible for the skywalk design. She asked how they could live with themselves all these years. She never heard back.

Olson has donated annually to a fund to build a memorial to remember the victims and pay tribute to rescue crews that night. She has heard that some people believe that families of the victims should have funded a memorial out of settlement proceeds.

That is another thing that makes her angry.

"I've really struggled with that," Olson said. "We didn't get a lot of money and even if we did, it's not about money. There is no price you can put on a family member's life."

If there was one person thrilled that the Hyatt started tea dances featuring big band music, Tom Henson was the guy.

"His only passion in life was big band music," said his daughter, Dorey DePuy. "He had 300 or 400 albums — Benny Goodman, Frank Sinatra, the Ink Spots."

Saturday morning was always Tommy Dorsey and pancakes at the Henson household, DePuy said. Henson was a very quiet man and had only one real friend, but the big band tunes brought him to life, she said.

DePuy grew up in a family of five children, which her father raised by himself after a divorce. He married again. Henson and his second wife, Romelia Henson, were at the tea dance when the skywalks fell. They were both killed. Tom Henson had every bone in his body broken, the family learned. The Independence, Mo., couple had one child of their own, a son, Joshua, 2 ½ years old. DePuy was 21 at the time.

DePuy thought her dad's death was both tragic and ironic in that he died while enjoying big band music — "doing what I only knew him to do." He was 46 when he died, his wife 29.

When DePuy was asked to identify his body that night from a Polaroid photograph, she was stunned to see that his face was swollen but not bloody.

"He was very peaceful looking," DePuy recalled. "I've never seen him look so peaceful."

In the 30 years since he died, DePuy can't escape the memory of how her dad and stepmother died. She works as a surgical instrument technician at Children's Mercy Hospital just up the street from the Hyatt and previously worked for 15 years at Waddell & Reed down the street in the other direction.

Every major work function seemed to be at the Hyatt, she said, resurrecting her disgust that her dad, stepmother and so many other people died unnecessarily.

"It was just sickening," she said. "Every time I went in there I wanted to spit on the floor. I am not that kind of person and I didn't do it, but I wanted to."

Today, DePuy passes the Hyatt every day in a shuttle bus to work

Aaron Leimkuehler, The Star

Jennifer Whiting of Lee's Summit, Mo., was a child in 1981 who pleaded with her grandparents not to go to the dance. They listened.

at Children's Mercy. Somehow, time has made the presence of the building less disconcerting. She thinks less about her dad's and stepmother's deaths and more about their lives.

"After these 30 years, I remember fondly the way they were," DePuy said. "It's bittersweet."

■ ■ ■

Over the years, there have been many stories about people who almost went to the Hyatt that night. Two of them were Bette and Gene Shepard in Independence, Mo.

Jennifer Whiting, their granddaughter who was 9 at the time, woke

141

up that morning determined to spend the night at their house after "chickening out" several times earlier because she wasn't quite ready. She called her grandparents, but they were already getting dressed for the tea dance at the Hyatt.

"I was devastated," Whiting said. "I cried and begged until they finally relented and canceled their plans."

Whiting was with her grandparents at Wet Woody's Water Slide in Independence that evening when they heard endless sirens coming from Kansas City. They would soon learn the awful reason.

For years, until her death two years ago, Bette Shepard would contend that Jennifer had saved their lives by insisting to spend that night at their house. And every Christmas she would give her grand-daughter an angel to hang on the tree.

"I am 38 years old now and have a Christmas tree full of angels," Whiting said. One, too, is engraved on her grandmother's headstone.

When she hangs the angels on her tree each Christmas Whiting remembers people who died at the Hyatt long ago, and she thinks, "it's almost as if the angels are them."

Jennifer Whiting's grandmother, Bette Shepard of Independence, always said Jennifer was her guardian angel for convincing her and her husband not to attend the tea dance on July 17, 1981. Every Christmas until her death two years ago, Shepard gave Whiting an angel ornament, including this one, to hang on her tree.

Aaron Leimkuehler, The Star

AFTERWORD

The most visible reminder of the Hyatt skywalks disaster is the towering hotel itself.

Many people want something else. Money is being raised to build a memorial to honor people who died or were injured in the skywalks collapse and to pay tribute to rescue workers.

Established in 2006, the Skywalk Memorial Foundation had raised about $350,000 through the end of May for the memorial. The goal is $1 million for the design, construction and landscaping at a site in Hospital Hill Park just east of the hotel.

Frank Freeman, president and co-founder of the foundation, said a memorial is long overdue.

"Those 114 people should be remembered," said Freeman, whose partner, Roger Grigsby, died in the skywalks collapse. Freeman said support for a memorial has built slowly since the 20th anniversary of the collapse, when, he said, few seemed to back it.

Today, the foundation's website — www.skywalkmemorial.org — lists names of contributors and comments from donors and other supporters. Fundraising accelerated this year and part of the proceeds from this book will be dedicated to the memorial.

The memorial site sits high on a hillside at the southeast corner of 22nd Street and Gillham Road, overlooking the downtown skyline. Approved by the Kansas City Department of Parks and Recreation, the site is visible from hotel rooms on the north side of the Hyatt. It is just northwest of Children's Mercy Hospital in a recently renovated park setting.

Foundation board co-secretary John Sullivan, who lost his mother, Kathryn Sullivan, at the Hyatt, is concerned that the tragedy will recede from memory as the generations pass.

"Pretty soon it will just be something in a book unless there is some physical memory of it," Sullivan said.

Peggy Olson, who lost her father and sister, Gerald Coffey and Pamela Coffey, in the collapse, has given money annually for the memorial.

"I'd like to have a place to sit and think about my family without going to the cemetery," she said.

Brent Wright, co-secretary of the foundation board, said the memorial would go beyond honoring the dead and injured. He said it would pay tribute to firefighters, police, construction workers, doctors, emergency medical technicians and others who helped at the scene.

"They really made a heroic effort to do the best they could under difficult circumstances and should be recognized for that in a formal way," said Wright, whose mother and stepfather, Karen and Eugene Jeter, died in the skywalks collapse.

The tentative design of the memorial is of a circular-shaped stone and concrete plaza. It would have a seating area around circular bands of small embedded fiber optic lights, meant to replicate a ripple effect, said Lorie Doolittle-Bowman, the Kansas City architect who designed it. The tiny lights would be in the concrete base, pointing upwards.

The ripples are to reflect how an extensive number of people helped on the night of the disaster, Doolittle-Bowman said. They each had a role in trying to treat, save or console people at the scene, she said.

In the center of the plaza would be 114 lights to symbolize those who died. On outer rings would be more than 200 lights for those who were injured. There is also discussion of etching in stone the names of the 114 people who died.

The goal is to create a peaceful place where visitors and the loved ones of victims can reflect and meditate, Doolittle-Bowman said.

Memorials to victims of tragedies are common. There is one in downtown Oklahoma City near the site of the 1995 terrorist bombing that killed 168 people at the Alfred R. Murrah Federal Building. A memorial is being developed at the site of the World Trade Center in New York.

Locally, a memorial was built to six firefighters who died in 1988

The park on Hospital Hill, overlooking the Hyatt Regency hotel, is the site of the planned memorial to those who died and were injured and to those who helped in the rescue effort.

when a trailer full of explosives blew up in southeast Kansas City.

There is a memorial in Topeka, Kan., related to the Hyatt disaster. A 17-foot-high bronze statue was dedicated on the grounds of the Topeka Performing Arts Center in 2006 to honor four members of a mariachi musical group who died in the skywalks collapse.

The group, Mariachi Estrella de Topeka, was one of the first female mariachi groups in the United States. They had performed at the Hyatt earlier that evening, though not at the tea dance. Killed were Connie Alcala, Delores Carmona, Delores Galvan and Linda Scurlock.

David Chavez, nephew of Alcala, helped spearhead the Topeka memorial and is on the board of the Skywalk Memorial Foundation. He said the proposed memorial is a challenging but worthwhile project.

"All it takes is the courage of some people to work tirelessly to make sure it happens," Chavez said. "That's what the board has been doing since its inception."

Raising money is not easy in tough economic times, but Chavez said support for the memorial is widespread, given how many people had a connection to someone hurt or killed in the disaster.

"A lot of people were touched by it," Chavez said. The memorial, he said, "means a lot to people in Kansas City."

Cathy Pitts, who lost her parents — Ray and Laurette Glover — in the skywalks collapse, said the memorial is appropriate, given the significance of the event.

Olson agreed. The memorial will help people remember an event that never should have happened, she said.

"It's a big part of Kansas City and its history," Olson said.

— Kevin Murphy

145

Dan White

Members of the Skywalk Memorial Foundation Board and volunteers (from left): Heather McMichael, public relations; Lorie Doolittle-Bowman, architect and memorial designer; Brent Wright, director; Frank Freeman, board president and director; Sol Koenigsberg, honorary chairman of fundraising; Vince Ortega, director; Richard L. Berkley, honorary chairman of fundraising; Kathy Hardee, legal adviser; Amy Kesler, website designer. Not pictured: John Sullivan, director; David Chavez, director; and Bill Quatman, design and construction committee.

Dan White, who shot the photograph of the Skywalk Memorial Foundation board at left, was on the staff of The Kansas City Star at the time the skywalks collapsed. Some of the photographs he took on the night of the disaster are reproduced in this book. Chief among them are the ones that appear on Pages iii and iv.

THE 114 VICTIMS OF THE JULY 17, 1981, TRAGEDY

The people who died included military veterans, teachers, lawyers, homemakers,
secretaries, business owners and one child, a fifth-grader who played sports and the guitar.
This list was originally published in The Kansas City Star on July 15, 2001,
marking the 20th anniversary of the disaster.

Connie Alcala, 32, founded the all-women's Mariachi Estrella Band at her Topeka church. Four band members died.

John J. Alder, 74, of Fairway was senior partner in his law firm. His wife escaped injury.

Velma "Pat" Allen, 40, of Kansas City taught physical education at Palmer Junior High School in Independence.

Carol M. Andrews, 33, a Kansas City mother of two, was a receptionist.

Bonnie Tracy Wheeler Bartels, 39, and **William F. Bartels III, 38,** of Olathe were lifelong area residents. He was Spring Hill State Bank's assistant vice president. She worked for Lang Laboratories Inc.

Robert G. Barton, 56, of Kansas City, North, was a Farmland Industries accountant.

Juanita P. Bedene, 60, of Overland Park taught at Santa Fe Trail Elementary School and enjoyed hiking, fishing and picking blackberries.

Robert C. Beneteau, 44, of Parkville, a Marine Corps veteran and avid golfer, was a Fuller Brush Co. vice president.

Calvin W. Berges, 57, and **Florence S. Berges, 62,** of Gladstone left behind two daughters. A World War II veteran, he worked in General Motors' paint department. She was a Farmland Industries clerk.

John Bergman Jr., 30, of Shawnee was a lawyer. His mother, Pearl, also died.

Pearl L. Bergman, 58, of Lansing was a ward secretary for Munson Army Hospital at Fort Leavenworth.

Julia H. Boggess, 45, of Lenexa owned Courtney Jewelers in Mission and was past president of the Mission Mart Retailers Association.

J. Robert Bolton, 63, and **Julia Slaughter Bolton, 52,** of Chesterfield, Mo., were vacationing. He was a bank vice president. She was a job guidance counselor for the University of Missouri-St. Louis.

Henry O. Botnen, 51, of Overland Park was an AT&T supervisor, a Boy Scout consultant and a Korean War veteran. His injured wife survived.

Louis Bottenberg, 66, of Kansas City had retired from the Kansas City School District's audiovisual department. He played the mandolin and taught music and dance. His wife survived.

Jacqueline S. Brooks, 24, was celebrating a new sales job with Hilton Hotels.

Delores Carmona, 35, of Topeka was a Mariachi Estrella Band member.

Cathy Jean Carver, 32, of Mission taught at Fairfax Elementary School in Kansas City, Kan. She died Aug. 19, 1981, after 33 days in a coma.

Theodore Cast, 72, of Holden, Mo., was a World War II veteran who had retired from teaching high school industrial arts. His injured wife survived.

Gerald L. Coffey, 42, of Leavenworth took his youngest daughter, Pamela, 11, to the dance. Both died. He was a retired U.S. Army lieutenant colonel and vice president of a Leavenworth title firm.

Pamela Coffey, 11, of Leavenworth, a fifth-grader at Xavier School, enjoyed Girl Scouts, sports and playing the guitar.

James S. "Sam" Cottingham, 46, of Kansas City, a former Independence city attorney, helped found that city's Queen City Baseball League.

James E. Daugherty, 56, and **Barbara L. Daugherty, 52,** of Merriam were tea dance regulars. He was a General Services Administration mechanical engineer, a former Merriam civil defense director and a World War II veteran. She was a hospital volunteer. They had six children.

Judith M. Davis, 38, of Parkville was a teacher's aide and volunteer at Union Chapel Elementary School. Her husband survived.

Richard V. DeKruyff, 56, of Kansas City was Southeast Junior High School's vice principal, a World War II veteran and a big band fan. His wife stayed home to baby-sit grandchildren.

Christine J. DePriest, 22, of Kearney was a University of Missouri-Kansas City law student.

Calvin Detrick Jr., 66, of Merriam was a World War II veteran and president of a company that made rubber rollers for the printing industry.

Clifton Dial, 80, lived 25 years in Kansas City before moving to Portland, Ore. A retired insurance salesman, he played saxophone, clarinet and violin in Shriners orchestras.

John T. "Jeff" Dixon, 64, of Warrensburg was a decorated World War II Navy pilot who became a paraplegic after a 1955 Olathe plane crash. The final victim, he died Dec. 1, 1981.

Lois Lorene Jenkins Duncan, 62, of rural Excelsior Springs was a championship ballroom dancer who taught dance for decades.

Jeff Durham, 25, was a real estate agent and part-time Westport bartender.

Louis M. Farris, 42, of St. Joseph was a firefighter who had won dance contests in his hometown.

Carolyn Fiene, 48, of Gladstone was a TWA accountant who enjoyed square dancing.

Delores Galvan, 26, of Topeka was a Mariachi Estrella Band member and a civil engineering draftsman for the state of Kansas.

E.O. Gerster, 63, of Overland Park was a dentist who died two months after the collapse.

John J. Glaser, 58, of Kansas City was a former teacher who worked in investing and insurance.

Laurette Glover, 53, and **Ray Glover, 54,** of Merriam had attended multiple tea dances. He worked in music therapy. She taught at Milburn Junior High in the Shawnee Mission district.

Richard M. Goss Jr., 42, of Overland Park was president of Dick Goss & Associates Inc., an automobile supply firm in Mission.

Roger Grigsby, 38, was a Denny's Restaurant manager.

Oscar F. Grim, 61, of Kansas City, North, a self-employed industrial salesman, enjoyed big band music, especially "Satin Doll." He pushed his wife away as the skywalks fell. She survived.

Helen Jean Gruening, 47, and **William Gruening Jr., 48,** of Prairie Village were active in American Field Service. He was vice president of Central Forest Products. She was a sales representative for Scholastic Magazine Inc. They had three children.

Joseph Gubar, 56, of Kansas City, a World War II veteran, was a salesman for Broadway Supply Co. His injured wife survived.

Virginia E. Hackett, 66, of Kansas City, North, retired in 1980 as a bank controller.

Paul I. Hansen, 51, of Mission developed Johnson County real estate for 30 years. He was a Korean War veteran.

Mary Hazelbeck, 56, of Overland Park, worked for the Internal Revenue Service. Her husband survived.

Romelia "Romey" Henson, 29, and **Thomas F. Henson, 46,** of Independence liked long walks in the country. He was a Farmland Industries traffic analyst. They had a 2-year-old son, plus five children from his previous marriage.

Stephen Hershman, 59, of Overland Park was a Russian immigrant who lived 45 years in the Kansas City area.

Doris M. Hill, 56, and **Forest D. Hill, 58,** of Lenexa liked big band music. She was a registered nurse. A World War II veteran, he was

Shawnee Mission Medical Center's assistant director of material management.

Richard L. Houltberg, 53, of Overland Park, a management consultant and sports enthusiast, canceled an evening tennis match and instead went to the dance with his fiancee. She survived.

Carl Huntsucker Jr., 44, and **Sondra Campbell Huntsucker, 39,** of Raytown enjoyed the outdoors. He was a salesman and a military veteran. She was a Bendix Corp. computer programmer.

Eugene Jeter, 48, and **Karen Jeter, 37,** had been married two weeks. Both worked for Federated Insurance Companies. He was assistant manager of claims. She was the marketing manager.

Ima Jean Johnson, 50, of Kansas City was a Blue Cross and Blue Shield claims examiner.

Robert S. Jonas, 58, of Overland Park was a product promotion manager, a Jewish religion teacher and a World War II veteran. His wife survived.

Elizabeth D. Kolega, 58, of St. Joseph was a salesclerk who went to the Hyatt "out of curiosity," her son said.

Julia A. Lamar, 33, of Shawnee had just won an award for her telephone sales work at Hallmark Cards Inc.

Mary E. Lane, 57, of Merriam enjoyed dancing and comedic acting. She was a Sturgess Equipment Co. secretary.

William V. Longmoor, 56, of Overland Park, a great-nephew of William Volker, was a Research Medical Center trustee, World War II veteran and jazz enthusiast. His wife survived.

Thomas Mahvi, 54, of Lenexa, an Iran native, was microbiology department chairman at the University of Missouri-Kansas City School of Medicine.

Clara McClellan, 55, of Gladstone was a hospital nutrition assistant.

Charlotte McDowell, 37, of Kansas City left a St. Louis area teaching job to start a marketing business scheduling conventions, dances and parties.

Betty J. McLane, 57, and **William L. McLane, 57,** of Prairie Village were big band fans. A World War II veteran, he was a life insurance underwriter. She was a church volunteer. They had four children.

Betty Louise Miller, 55, of St. Joseph, a steakhouse hostess, was enjoying her first Friday off in more than a year.

David J. Miller, 51, of Overland Park was a Southgate State Bank executive vice president. His injured wife survived.

Vernon D. Mitchell, 52, of Independence was co-owner of Plaza Hardware Inc., a Business Men's Assurance Co. employee and a Korean War veteran. His injured wife survived.

Susan Moberg, 46, of Kansas City, Kan., was a psychic reader who worked for the Convention and Visitors Bureau of Greater Kansas City.

Sheryl Lynn Morgan, 33, of St. Joseph taught at William Jewell College.

Marjorie Ann Morris, 47, of Overland Park taught at Santa Fe Trail Elementary School in the Shawnee Mission district.

Nick Noble, 31, a foreign-car salesman, had lived in Kansas City five years.

Louise O'Connor, 62, and **Neal O'Connor, 64,** of Mission loved to dance. She had been a secretary. A World War II veteran, he had retired as Traders Bank's head cashier and controller.

Leona Omer, 69, of Greeley, Colo., was a widow who donated time to charities.

James M. Paolozzi, 39, of Kansas City directed network operations for Uninet Inc., a division of United Telecom Co. His wife survived.

Jerold M. Rau, 42, of Kansas City attended the dance with his wife and another couple, the Paolozzis. The men died; their wives survived. Rau was president of the Kansas City Dermatological Society.

Paul H. Rinehart, 46, of Overland Park was an automotive parts salesman for Dick Goss & Associates.

John M. Rodman, 78, of Kansas City was a retired automobile inspector for Fisher Body Co.

Ruby Mae Scanlon, 54, of Overland Park was a Nettleton Home board member. Her husband survived.

Linda L. Scurlock, 36, of Topeka was a Mariachi Estrella Band member and a Santa Fe railroad claims processor.

Floyd Sholts, 69, and **Violet Sholts, 62,** of Kansas City, North, left one daughter. He was a retired postal clerk. She was a retired pharmacy technician.

William E. Sigler, 61, and **Ruth T. Sigler, 57,** of Kansas City, North, liked square dancing. He was a Kansas City Power & Light Co. technician. She was a North Kansas City School District food service worker. They had four children.

Helen A. Stark, 26, of Kansas City was an insurance underwriter for the Mutual Benefit Life Insurance Co.

Edmund J. Stein III, 68, and Viola E. Stein, 65, of Overland Park. He sold advertising and was a World War II veteran. She sold Avon and enjoyed gardening. They had four children.

David Stover, 50, of Dubuque, Iowa, capped a two-week vacation with his wife by visiting Raymore friends. The friends died. Stover's injured wife survived. He was an engineer for John Deere & Co.

Kathryn Anne Sullivan, 45, of Blue Springs was a doctor's receptionist attending her first tea dance.

Lucille M. Taylor, 69, of Kansas City was active in her church.

Anna F. Terry, 53, of Kansas City, Kan., was a widow and a Visiting Nurses Association secretary. Her husband had been killed in 1979 by robbery suspects he was chasing.

Robert F. Torrey, 53, and Mary E. Torrey, 49, of Roeland Park were known for generosity. He was a sales manager for Sealright Co. and a Korean War veteran. She worked in accounting at the Panhandle Eastern Pipe Line Co. They had two daughters.

John H. Tvedten Sr., 50, of Kansas City was a Kansas City Fire Department battalion chief whose son, John, later died fighting a Kansas City fire.

Lynn Vander Heyden, 22, of Shawnee was a senior at Rockhurst College. She was headed for Skies, the rotating restaurant atop the Hyatt.

Karyn T. Walsh, 41, of Kansas City was a PBX operator for William Volker & Co.

Lawrence Watson, 37, and Suzanne Watson, 34, of Parkville enjoyed music and nostalgia. He was vice president of American Dish Service. They had four children.

Linda K. Wharton, 26, of Lake Quivira was a manager for Sears, Roebuck and Co.

Edward A. Whitney, 60, and Joyce B. Whitney, 49, of Raymore. He was general manager of the Cox Hide Co. in Belton, a Heart of America Soccer Association state commissioner and a World War II veteran. She worked part time for Cox Hide and volunteered at a hospital. They had two children.

Ferna M. Wicker, 52, of Overland Park enjoyed church volunteer work. Her uninjured husband survived.

Kathleen O. Wilber, 55, of Leawood grew up on a Kansas farm and enjoyed riding horses. Her husband survived.

James E. Williams Jr., 42, of Oak Grove was a Social Security Administration investigator and an Oak Grove volunteer firefighter.

Paul W. Winett, 38, of Shawnee, was treasurer of Paragon Products Inc., and a military veteran.

Rudolph E. Zatezalo, 60, of Kansas City was a Missouri Democratic political figure, World War II veteran and former bank vice president. His wife survived.